DOUBLE DISCRIMINATION

ISSUES AND SERVICES FOR PEOPLE WITH LEARNING DIFFICULTIES FROM BLACK AND ETHNIC MINORITY COMMUNITIES

Carol Baxter
Kamaljit Poonia
Linda Ward
Zenobia Nadirshaw

Cartoons by Angela Martin

King's Fund Centre / Commission for Racial Equality
December 1990

Published by the King's Fund Centre in conjunction with the Commission for Racial Equality
126 Albert Street
London
NW1 7NF

Tel: 071 267 6111

ISBN 0 903060 795

A CIP catalogue record for this book is available from the British Library

Distributed by BEBC
9 Albion Close
Parkstone
Poole
Dorset
BH12 3LL

The King's Fund Centre is a health services development agency which promotes improvements in health and social care. We do this by working with people in health services, in social services, in voluntary agencies, and with the users of their services. We encourage people to try out new ideas, provide financial or practical support to new developments, and enable experiences to be shared through workshops, conferences and publications. Our aim is to ensure that good developments in health and social care are widely taken up.

The King's Fund Centre is a part of the
King Edward's Hospital Fund for London.

Printed by: AFS Images Offset, London.

CONTENTS

Acknowledgements

This project — and handbook — would not have come about without the help and support of many people.

Our thanks are due first to the King's Fund Centre for encouraging us to pursue the initial idea for the project and, most importantly, for subsequently funding it — and to the Commission for Racial Equality for their financial support also.

The project benefited during its lifetime from the thoughts, experience and time of our Advisory Group — Cathie Lloyd and Chris Ranger (CRE), Gillian Loughran (London Based Training Consortium), Silu Pascoe (Cornwall Social Services Department), Joan Rush (King's Fund Centre), Karen Saleswki (Brent Social Services Department) —- for which we thank them.

Many individuals gave helpful suggestions and comments at different stages of the project. We owe a special thanks to Naomi Connelly, Peter Ferns, Gus John, Oliver Russell and Derek Thomas for their encouragement.

A large number of people in community health councils, health authorities, local education authorities and social services departments throughout the country gave their time, consideration and energy to completing our various questionnaires. We hope that this handbook will make them feel their effort was worthwhile.

A project such as this involves constant typing and retyping of chapter drafts. Our thanks to the various secretaries who have assisted in this process — especially Penny Bell and Di Pelley. Thanks too to Maggie Pearson for her editing skills.

Our biggest debt, of course, is to the many individuals, families, front line staff and managers who gave us their time. They shared their (sometimes painful) experiences with us in order to enrich this handbook, and, we hope, to improve the services available to people with learning difficulties from black and ethnic minority communities in the future.

Norah Fry Research Centre
University of Bristol

September 1990

Carol Baxter and Kamaljit Poonia were formerly Research Associates at the University of Bristol, Norah Fry Research Centre, where Linda Ward is Research Fellow. Zenobia Nadirshaw is Consultant Clinical Psychologist, North West Hertfordshire Health Authority.

Definition of Terms

Defining terms to describe people and intricate aspects of their life experiences is always very difficult and often unsatisfactory. Many of the terms used in this handbook are, therefore, merely a compromise. We are aware that some readers may be coming across them for the first time, so it is important that we clarify some of the more controversial terms as follows.

Black and Ethnic Minority

This term is used to include all members of minority racial groups in Britain. We are aware that there are many people from ethnic minority communities who do not always identify themselves as black, yet share a common experience of discrimination and inequality as a result of their ethnic origin, language, culture or religion. We use both terms together to include anyone who suffers the effects of racism.

Afro-Caribbean

Persons of African origin who were born in one of the Caribbean Islands and their descendants born in the UK. It is a positive term of identity used by a growing number of people from these backgrounds.

Asian

Persons born in India, Pakistan or Bangladesh and the descendants of such persons who were born in East Africa. It also includes their descendants born in the UK. The persons to whom the term is applied may not necessarily define themselves as Asians, or if they do, may not recognise it as a predominant self-identity.

Both of the above terms refer to a wide range of people who do not share a common culture.

Racism

All people can hold prejudiced beliefs about people whom they see as different on account of their origins or ethnic group, but racism can be attributed only to those who have the power to turn their prejudice into acts of discrimination or unfair treatment. Acts of discrimination can be conscious or unconscious. Racism operates at two different levels, individual and institutional.

Individual or direct racism occurs when a person treats people unfairly because of their racial or ethnic origins. Most people, especially those of us working in the caring professions, would not see ourselves as racist in this way.

Institutional or indirect racism which forms part of our organisations and services is the more common and damning form of racism. This happens in a variety of ways:

➢ by default, that is, the ways in which things are done do not take into account the needs of people from black and ethnic minority communities

— for example, the catering facilities in services for people with learning difficulties are on the whole based on what is usually eaten by the majority white population

➢ where people with a position of power base their decisions on "racist" assumptions and stereotypes

— for example, black and ethnic minority people care for their own and, therefore, do not need our support services

➢ where rules and regulations of an organisation apply to all but they have the effect of excluding black and ethnic minority people while maintaining the privileged position of white people

— for example, the qualifications of doctors and other professionals trained abroad are often not professionally recognised in this country

Learning Difficulties

We have chosen to use the term "people with learning difficulties" instead of "people with mental handicap" because that is the term generally preferred by service users themselves.

Introduction

Services for Whom ?

The Government recognises that people from different cultural backgrounds may have particular care needs and problems. Minority communities may have different concepts of community care and it is important that service providers are sensitive to these variations. Good community care will take account of the circumstances of minority communities and will be planned in consultation with them.

(Caring for People, 1989)

We live in a multiracial society yet most of the key literature on developing services for people with learning difficulties has ignored this fact (Audit Commission, 1986; King's Fund Centre, 1980). Most national, regional and local plans for service development in this area show a similarly "colour blind" approach. The particular experiences, circumstances and needs of black and ethnic minority children and adults with learning difficulties and their families are ignored, or assumed (often incorrectly) to be the same as those of their white peers. The shortcomings of such a "colour blind" approach — in which a uniform service is supposed to be equally accessible and appropriate to people in maybe very different circumstances and with different needs — are well documented (Pearson, 1985; Ahmed, Cheetham and Small, 1986). Nonetheless, the approach persists, even amongst those

advocating what are commonly thought to be 'progressive' policies for people with learning difficulties — that is, policies based upon the principles of normalisation, the pursuit of social integration, valued opportunities and "ordinary lives". Only now are the white cultural assumptions underpinning current community care policies being recognised, their limitations understood and their relevance to services for people with learning difficulties from black and ethnic minority communities challenged.

In Britain, black and ethnic minority people experience discrimination and disadvantage in almost every aspect of their lives: in housing and employment (Brown, 1984), education (DES, 1985) and health (McNaught, 1984; Torkington, 1983; Marmot et al, 1984). They consistently receive less than their entitlement to benefits and services (Gohil, 1987). It is hardly surprising, therefore, that there is serious cause for concern that the needs of black and ethnic minority people with learning difficulties may be unmet and that services for them leave much to be desired (e.g. Cocking and Athwal 1990). Fundamental issues like access, information and the need to develop an approach which is sensitive to all traditions and backgrounds, have still to be addressed.

There is a stigma attached to having a learning difficulty. Being black as well means a double disadvantage. Now — when services for people with learning difficulties are poised for the changes heralded by the NHS and Community Care Act — there are opportunities for change. As new patterns of support are developed, all those involved in services for people with learning difficulties (whether as planners, providers, carers or users) can perhaps seize the moment to create services designed to meet the needs of *everyone* in our multiracial society.

BRITAIN'S BLACK AND ETHNIC MINORITY POPULATION

➢ 4.5% of the total British population are born in the New Commonwealth and Pakistan.

➢ Over 43% of the black population is British born.

➢ 80% of young Afro-Caribbean adults are British born.

➢ 3% of the black population are of pensionable age.

> 20% of Afro-Caribbeans
> 13% of Asians } are over the age of 45

➢ 50% of the population of some cities and boroughs are from black and ethnic minority communities.

SOURCE: BROWN (1984)

What this Handbook is About

People with learning difficulties come in all colours and from all ethnic backgrounds, but everyone tends to ignore this ... And it really is an issue that is important. The fact that you have a learning difficulty will not save you from being the victim of racism — nor will it immunise you against picking up racist attitudes.

(CMH, 1988)

Many service providers would like to improve the quality of service they provide to black and ethnic minority people with learning difficulties. Many do not know where to start; others need support and advice.

As one white service manager told us:

We are failing miserably in this area ... we must get our act together.

Another wrote:

At present, I work in a network of small houses in the community providing care for adults with learning difficulties, and have tried to put a lot of thought into how the service we provide meets the needs of black clients.

I have been working particularly closely with a young man from an Afro-Caribbean background. It has concerned me that none of the workers on our team, nor any of the people with whom we have any degree of close contact, are black, and hence can have experienced racism from a personal perspective. As this client has no speech and only very limited communication otherwise, this poses quite considerable problems when trying to assess reactions and situations; we can only guess.

Furthermore, in trying to meet his cultural needs, we face the problem of a largely white service providing services for its users, which inevitably means that those in a minority have very few culturally relevant or accessible services available. At present, our few attempts to initiate a more appropriate service have been confined to the West Indian Social Club, where we have found some reasonable leisure facilities, but in terms of service provision we have met with little response from management etc.

It is doubtless that people with a mental handicap who are from an ethnic minority often face double discrimination in their day to day life, and with the higher community presence given by the prevailing community care model, individuals are more exposed to this.

... It is very difficult for me, a white worker, to judge accurately and objectively about the extent to which this individual, and other black people with learning difficulties, suffer from "double discrimination" short of acknowledging that they do to some extent.

This handbook is a response to the concern about the lack of information on good services for people with learning difficulties from black and ethnic minority communities. Previous discussions and action in this field have tended to be disjointed and ad hoc. This handbook brings together the limited amount of work that has been done so far in this area. Its primary aim is to provide practical suggestions for service improvements. It is written from an antiracist perspective taking black and ethnic minority people's experience of racism and discrimination as its starting point and deals with different aspects of services through questions, information and highlighting good practice.

Much of our attention has been focused on Afro-Caribbean and Asian communities. They are the two largest groups of ethnic minorities in Britain and significantly more information is available about them. Most of the issues identified in this handbook, however, are relevant to anyone who suffers from discrimination because of colour, religion, custom or race.

The innovative projects, schemes and programmes which we have highlighted are vulnerable to budget cuts and staff changes. Some of those we have identified may no longer exist in their original form. They do, however, demonstrate that changes can be made. All have some positive features which are worth sharing. However, we wish to emphasise that many of these projects are struggling to maintain a service on a very small budget. Staff resources are often over-stretched. We would ask readers to exercise restraint in contacting these projects directly. If you feel that contact would be useful, please be mindful that the amount of time and money they have available to spend helping other organisations may be limited.

WHAT IT IS NOT

This handbook is *not* a definitive guide or blueprint on how to create antiracist services. It is only a starting point.

It does not make any attempt to provide cultural information about black and ethnic minority people. Rather, it encourages the reader to find out for themselves the needs, wants and wishes of individuals and their families which can then inform changes in practice. We realise that this is a large agenda and that we have only skimmed the surface. We hope that it will encourage future initiatives which will build, and improve upon, this first attempt.

What We Did

We conducted a national postal survey of health and education authorities, social services departments and community health councils. Questionnaires asking about issues, services and examples of good practice were sent out to all authorities in areas estimated to have over 4.5% of their population from black and ethnic minority communities. Responses to the questionnaire revealed a varied and disparate picture of the way agencies were, or were not, tackling these issues. Some authorities sent us their equal opportunities policies and/or examples of good practice in local service provision. Few had detailed action plans for change. Material from the questionnaire responses is included throughout the book.

We visited innovative schemes and services run by statutory and voluntary organisations and self-help groups.

To get a clearer picture of what services on the ground were really like for black and ethnic minority people with learning difficulties and their families, we looked in detail at the services available in two different areas of the country, both with a significant black/ethnic minority population: one in the North West and one in the South West.

By far the most significant and revealing part of our work was visiting and talking with people with learning difficulties and their families and carers.

Who is it For ?

This handbook should be of interest to anyone involved in the field of learning difficulties. We hope it will be relevant to people working at all levels within statutory and voluntary organisations, either as service planners, managers or providers of care and support on a day to day basis.

We hope this handbook will provide an affirming experience for black staff, giving them greater confidence to participate in service planning and developments for black and ethnic minority users.

Finding Your Way Around

The handbook has been designed in three clear sections.

Chapter 1 looks at key issues and concepts in the development of services for people with learning difficulties and assesses their relevance to a multiracial society.

Chapters 2–6 look at services for people with learning difficulties and their families at different stages in their life cycle, starting with the birth of a child and going through to ageing, death and bereavement. Issues which are addressed in one chapter often apply to other age groups, particularly in relation to the kinds of services and support which people need. We have tended to deal with an issue in detail in one specific chapter, cross-referencing to other chapters where it is also pertinent. We are aware that, in real life, distinctions between different age groups are not this clear cut, but we have presented our ideas and material in this way for the sake of convenience and to avoid repetition.

Chapters 7–8 focus on issues and themes which cut across services. *Chapter 7* looks at the position of black and ethnic minority service providers and the organisational and professional aspects of staffing and employment. *Chapter 8* looks at what individuals and organisations can do from here onwards. It gives practical suggestions to both managers and care providers about taking the issues forward in their personal areas of work. *Chapters 7 and 8* will be of particular importance to managers and others involved with developing and implementing equal opportunity employment policies and strategies for service provision.

Each chapter starts with an introduction to the content. Material is presented in various forms:

➢ discussion of issues and principles

➢ practical information

➢ secondary issues which need expanding (in boxes)

➢ illustrations and examples in the form of quotations, people's individual stories, interview extracts (presented in italics)

➢ "Ideas in Practice" in specific projects and schemes (in boxes)

➢ references, further reading, resources and organisations (listed at the end of each chapter)

How to Use this Handbook

This handbook may be read from cover to cover. We have, however, tried to design it for use in a variety of ways:

➢ as a base line for service planners and managers to review services in their particular areas

➢ as a source of ideas for individual service providers

➢ to provide recommendations for Community Health Councils, community groups and voluntary organisations wishing to raise issues with authorities in their area

➢ to highlight the main implications for training and service development

➢ to identify areas for further investigation and development locally

References

Ahmed S, Cheetham J and Small J (1986): *Social Work with Black Children and Their Families*. London, Batsford.

Audit Commission (1986): *Making a Reality of Community Care*. London, HMSO.

Brown C (1984): *Black and White Britain. The Third PSI Survey*. London, Gower.

Caring for People. Community Care in the Next Decade and Beyond (1989). London, HMSO.

Campaign for Mental Handicap (CMH) (1988): "Ethnic minorities — And about time too". *CMH Newsletter,* Winter 1988–89. No 55, p 2.

Cocking I and Athwal S (1990): "A special case for special treatment". *Social Work Today,* 8 February, pp 12–13.

DES (1985): *Education for All. The Report of the Committee of Enquiry into the Education of Children from Ethnic Minority Groups (The Swann Report)*. London, HMSO.

Gohil V (1987): "DHSS service delivery to ethnic minority claimants". *Leicester Rights Bulletin,* June/July, No 32, pp 7–8.

King's Fund Centre (1980): *An Ordinary Life*. London, King's Fund Centre.

Marmot M, Adelstein A and Bulusu L (1984): *Immigrant Mortality in England and Wales, 1970–1978*. OPCS Studies of Medical and Population Subjects, 47. London, HMSO.

McNaught A (1984): *Race and Health Care in the United Kingdom*. London, Centre for Health Services Management Studies, Polytechnic of South Bank.

Pearson M A (1985): *Equal Opportunities in the NHS. A Handbook*. Cambridge, National Extension College/Training in Health and Race.

Torkington N P K (1983): *The Racial Politics of Health — A Liverpool Profile*. Liverpool, Merseyside Area Profile Group, Department of Sociology, University of Liverpool.

CHALLENGING ASSUMPTIONS

I respect your need for you to exist independently of your child, but that is your need. My need is totally different because my life is interwoven with my child's life and I want that to be.

ASIAN MOTHER

INTRODUCTION

In writing this handbook, we have set out to provide practical suggestions on how services may be improved. But before doing this, it is important to look at the principles and assumptions which currently underpin the services provided.

Many services for people with learning difficulties are now undergoing reform, often on the basis of new philosophies geared towards change. But we need to exercise caution. The relevance of some of these concepts to the lives of many black and ethnic minority people in our society is not necessarily clear. With the best will in the world, black and ethnic minority people with learning difficulties could be further disadvantaged by "progressive" developments which are inappropriate to their needs.

This chapter examines four key philosophies and approaches which currently influence the delivery of community services and assesses their relevance to a multiracial society.

➢ Community Care

➢ Normalisation

➢ Individual Programme Planning

➢ Assessment

Other key concepts and practices are reviewed in later chapters.

Community Care

The pattern of welfare provision in the UK is changing. The change which will have the biggest impact on the lives of people with learning difficulties is the increased emphasis on care in the community. Large institutions are contracting or closing down. More and more people with learning difficulties are living in the community.

The Government White Paper *Caring for People* (1989) highlights changes in the way community care — including those services for people with learning difficulties — is to be managed. Local authorities will have responsibility for assessing people's needs and ensuring that appropriate services are provided. They will contract out or buy in services from voluntary and other agencies as well as provide services themselves. It is expected that voluntary organisations and families will provide more services and take over responsibilities for activities which were previously the responsibility of social services departments.

In acknowledging the needs of black communities the Griffiths report emphasised "both policy and action need to respond to the multiracial nature of British society" (Griffiths, 1988). However, the implications of the White Paper for people with learning difficulties from black and ethnic minority communities raise several concerns.

> Mainstream voluntary organisations in our society do not cater adequately for the needs of black and ethnic minority communities (Dungate, 1984). They are largely managed by white staff who are not always aware of the needs and wishes of potential black and ethnic minority consumers. They are not, therefore, in a position to assess either the quality or quantity of services needed by these communities, whom they rarely consult. When these organisations bid for contracts in the future, they cannot, however, be asked to pursue a specific equal opportunities policy (although local authorities will be able to ask them what provisions they are making under the Race Relations Act).

➤ Black and ethnic minority communities are continually setting up voluntary services in response to unmet needs and to counteract discrimination by existing (statutory) services. More pressing issues, however, such as homelessness, racial harassment and immigration problems, mean that the needs of people with learning difficulties are inevitably low among their priorities for action.

➤ Under *Caring for People* and the ensuing *NHS and Community Care Act*, statutory agencies will be required to develop contractual relationships with the voluntary and private sector. There will be a move away from grants to voluntary groups towards contracts instead. Many small voluntary organisations (like those run by black and ethnic minority communities) will not be well placed to tender for contracts.

— They may not be well informed about the workings of statutory agencies, or what resources are available, or how to get them.

— The particular strengths and approaches of black and ethnic minority organisations are rarely recognised by statutory agencies. (For example, black and ethnic minority organisations often have a more holistic approach to meeting needs than is found in the white voluntary sector. Services tend not to be compartmentalised — one organisation may provide a variety and range of services. Similarly, black churches play a major role in caring for and supporting people. This is often neither recognised nor appreciated.)

— Many black and ethnic minority voluntary organisations are already under-resourced and, therefore, deprived of the secure managerial and financial base required to attract more funds.

Many voluntary organisations in the black and ethnic minority communities which are currently undertaking vital work will have to change dramatically if they are to successfully tender for contracts. It is not at all clear that this degree of change is feasible or, indeed, desirable. (For details of an information pack on contracts and black and ethnic minority organisations, see the *Resources* section at the end of this chapter.)

➤ The majority of black and ethnic minority people with learning difficulties already live at home. At present their families often cope without much support from health or social services. They will not benefit from the funding currently targeted at resettling people from institutions in the community.

Caring for People — The White Paper on Community Care

The Race Equality Unit at NISW (National Institute for Social Work) recommended that in order to meet the community care needs of black and ethnic minority people, the White Paper should:

➤ make reference to equal opportunities and recognise the need for antiracist and antidiscriminatory strategies for providing services for black and minority ethnic populations

➤ clarify the statutory duties and legal responsibilities that community care planners, service providers and co-ordinators and assessors have for providing appropriate and adequate services to black and minority ethnic populations

➤ acknowledge the diverse and differing needs of black and minority ethnic populations as an essential pre-requisite for providing different community care services as opposed to the "same" approach adopted for white and majority ethnic populations

➤ validate the contributions made by black and minority ethnic voluntary organisations in providing community care services and strongly recommend support and resources from mainstream authorities and agencies to these organisations

➤ recommend positive action to negotiate with and award contracts to black and minority ethnic voluntary organisations and groups

➤ give explicit guidance to local authorities about the allocation of budgets (care element of social security budget) for private and voluntary residential care establishments catering for black and minority ethnic communities

➤ require that all community care planners, providers, co-ordinators and assessors consult black and minority ethnic users, carers and service providing groups in planning and resourcing community care services and provide information about services to black and minority ethnic communities

➤ make it mandatory for statutory agencies to assess in their local profiles the demographic construction of black and minority ethnic communities in their areas and their present service access

➤ make specific recommendations for the recruitment of black and minority ethnic staff and provision of antiracist training for all staff responsible for designing and delivering packages of care

➤ give special attention to the criteria for assessment to be undertaken by people with appropriate awareness, understanding and knowledge of the needs of community care of black and minority ethnic communities and include right of appeal

➤ prioritise both quantitative and qualitative monitoring of all community care services for black and minority ethnic communities as an essential part of community care policies and practices, and recommend representation of black and minority ethnic users, carers and service providing groups in the monitoring process

➤ recognise the need for national guidance on the quantity and quality of community care services that are able to respond to the needs of black and minority ethnic users and carers; and recommend the establishment of a working group with black and minority ethnic involvement and representation

(From Dutt (ed), 1989)

In the event, the White Paper confined its consideration of services for black and ethnic minority people to the three sentences quoted at the beginning of this handbook (page 1).

Normalisation

The principles of normalisation are intended to guide service managers, staff and others in their interactions with people with learning difficulties, and in the planning and delivery of services. They are based on the belief that people with learning difficulties (and other vulnerable people) should be socially accepted and valued, with the same rights as other, non-handicapped, people to live in the mainstream of society as valued and respected citizens.

The principles of normalisation, now sometimes referred to as "social role valorisation" (Wolfensberger, 1983), are often presented in complex language. Put at their simplest, the aims are threefold:

➤ to enable people with learning difficulties to lead lives which are as "normal" or "valued" as possible

➤ to achieve this by "valued" means (for example, through the ordinary services used by other people in the community — like ordinary houses, schools, employment and leisure facilities — rather than segregated special services used only by handicapped people)

➤ to change people's attitudes, so that individuals with learning difficulties are seen in a more positive light, and respected and valued like other people in the community

(OPEN UNIVERSITY, 1986)

The main significance for service planners and providers is the encouragement to promote systems and practices which are tailored to the individual and accepted and valued in the wider society.

Potentially then, normalisation should be a force for good in service development. However, all philosophies encompass and reflect firmly entrenched social values and beliefs. While forcefully challenging certain sets of values and beliefs which we take for granted in our society (for example, negative assumptions about people with learning difficulties generally), normalisation itself makes certain blanket assumptions about what is "normal" or "valued" in our society, as we shall discuss below. Before indiscriminately applying these principles two key questions must be answered:

➤ What are the norms which our society takes for granted?

➤ What kind of values should be involved in deciding on policy and practice?

Normalisation

Some Definitions

➤ letting people with learning difficulties obtain "an existence as close to the normal as possible …" (Bank-Mikkelson, 1969)

➤ enabling people with learning difficulties to enjoy "patterns and conditions of everyday life which are as close as possible to the norms and patterns of the mainstream of society" (Nirje, 1970)

➤ "The most explicit and highest goal of normalisation must be the creation, support and defence of valued social roles for people who are at risk of social devaluation" (Wolfensberger, 1983)

And Some Questions

➤ In our multicultural society, can professionals be sure that they know what is "normal" or "valued" for *all* their potential "clients" ?

➤ Can we be confident that service planners and managers, who are largely white, know how to interpret and implement the principles of normalisation in ways that are positive and meaningful for black and ethnic minority people with learning difficulties and their families — whose life circumstances and aspirations may differ fundamentally from their own ?

➤ If the goal of normalisation is to create and defend "valued social roles for people who are at risk of social devaluation", how can we use these principles to challenge the dual devaluation experienced by black and ethnic minority people with learning difficulties in our society ?

Taking White Values as the Norm

Britain is a multiracial, multilingual and multicultural society in which black and ethnic minority people are devalued, disadvantaged and discriminated against. Authority and decision making are generally in the hands of white people, and, within services, professional policy and practice are determined by them. Consequently, the needs, wants and wishes of the white majority are considered "normal" or "valued" and become part of standard or desired provision. Any specifically different needs of black and ethnic minority service users will tend to be ignored. Styles of dress, behaviour, or patterns of lifestyle which differ from the white norm, but are valued by ethnic minority groups are unlikely to be valued and pursued by white service providers on their clients' behalf. (See box top right, *Normalisation and the "Conservative Corollary".*)

Normalisation and the "Conservative Corollary"

What is the "Conservative Corollary" ?

For devalued people, activities, styles of dress and other outward appearances which would not in themselves cause comment if exhibited by valued people, can combine to reinforce the devalued state ...

Providing positive compensation for this state of affairs means to address oneself more to the issues than would be the case for someone not at risk of devaluation and try for:

1. the best physical appearance

2. greater opportunities for valued behaviour

3. generally veering to the "conservative" side of appearance and behaviour

(RACE, 1987)

Cause for Concern

When white staff attempt to implement the "conservative corollary" of normalisation on behalf of their black and ethnic minority clients, they are likely to encourage styles of dress, appearance and behaviour which are valued by the white majority population — at the expense of those valued by black and ethnic minority people themselves ...

A simple exercise carried out by Harlesden Community Mental Handicap Team highlighted how services provided on the basis of what white professionals would value for themselves would in many cases conflict directly with other cultures. People from the local Afro-Caribbean and Asian communities were asked to consider statements from their own perspective and place them on a scale from one (valued) to five (not valued). The statements were designed to measure attitudes to:

➤ living independently

➤ relationships with family members

➤ relationships with the opposite sex

➤ leisure time activities

➤ self esteem and racial identity

A group of white service managers and key personnel were given the same exercise. The results contrasted very significantly. Some statements which reflect concepts quite central to normalisation (having a boyfriend/ girlfriend; going to a pub/disco; being extrovert) which were positively valued by the white professionals were negatively valued by people from black and ethnic minority communities, and vice versa. There were also significant differences in the responses given by the Afro-Caribbean and Asian samples. (See table overleaf.)

RACE AND MENTAL HANDICAP WORKSHOP — NORMALISATION EXERCISE

The exercise was completed by 30 people — 10 of Afro-Caribbean, 10 of Asian and 10 of White British and Irish origin who lived in Harlesden, London Borough of Brent, in Autumn 1985.

	POSITIVE			NEGATIVE		
	1	2	3	4	5	SAMPLE
Living independently	10					Afro-Caribbean
			5		5	Asian
	7		3			White
Being good at sewing	2		4	4		Afro-Caribbean
			5		5	Asian
	2		6		2	White
Having a boyfriend/girlfriend	2	4	4			Afro-Caribbean
					10	Asian
	5		1		4	White
Eating with your fingers	2		4	4		Afro-Caribbean
	8	2				Asian
					10	White
Being black †	10					Afro-Caribbean
	10					Asian
	2	2	3		3	White
Being severely mentally handicapped					10	Afro-Caribbean
				2	8	Asian
					10	White
Remaining closely linked to your family in adult life	10					Afro-Caribbean
	10					Asian
		4	5		1	White
Going to pubs/discos	2	2	2		4	Afro-Caribbean
				2	8	Asian
	5	2	3			White
Wearing a sari			4		6	Afro-Caribbean
	8	2				Asian
	1		6	1	2	White
Being extrovert	2	2	4	2		Afro-Caribbean
			5	2	3	Asian
	5	2	2		1	White
Drinking alcohol	2		4	4		Afro-Caribbean
				2	8	Asian
	3	2	4		1	White

† For Afro-Caribbean and Asian samples, self; for White sample, of a friend.

A service provider explained to us how his ideas on what was "normal" or "valued" had changed through his involvement with a young Afro-Caribbean woman with learning difficulties:

I thought that Beverley was not getting the right sort of stimulation, opportunities or experiences at home. Meals and bedtime were never regular and there were always relatives and friends passing through. Much of the weekend was spent preparing for and attending church. The family life seemed chaotic. I tried to convince her parents to send Beverley to a nearby Adult Training Centre but they were not interested. This, to me, suggested that they were preoccupied with their own activities and did not really understand the importance of this for Beverley's development. Then I began to think again. Beverley was after all well adjusted. The variety of activity and people around her as well as her involvement in the church were quite enriching. They kept her occupied and gave her a sense of belonging. The activities at the Adult Training Centre could not replace all this nor were they of any relevance to her family and the community in which she lives.

PASS and Services for Black and Ethnic Minority People

PASS (Program Analysis of Service Systems) is a comprehensive system for evaluating the extent to which services are implementing normalisation principles (Wolfensberger and Glenn, 1975). PASSING (Program Analysis of Service Systems: Implementation of Normalisation Goals) is similarly used to judge how well services are doing normalisation-wise, looking in particular at how a service supports devalued people's social image and their competence or abilities (Wolfensberger and Thomas, 1983).

PASS and PASSING evaluations can be a powerful force for change in services, helping those involved see the limitations of the service they are providing and practical ways in which that service can be improved. There are, however, a number of concerns about PASS in relation to services for black and ethnic minority people with learning difficulties.

➢ Some services are becoming aware that it is inappropriate to have exclusively white staff serving black and ethnic minority clients. The employment of black and ethnic minority staff can contribute significantly to the development of better services for black and ethnic minority people, as we shall see later (Chapter 7). However, services which make active attempts to recruit black staff — so that the composition of the staff group reflects more accurately that of the user population — would be penalised under a traditional PASS evaluation. One particular rating guideline (termed "deviant staff juxtaposition") suggests that because black and ethnic minority people have low social status their employment in services for people with learning difficulties should be avoided, as their presence may further devalue their clients in the eyes of the wider society.

➤ Almost all the people trained to undertake PASS evaluations in this country are white. There is, therefore, a real risk that their assessment of the environment and lifestyle of black and ethnic minority service users — a setting's internal design and decorations, individuals' personal appearance, activities and routines, labels and forms of address — will inevitably, albeit unconsciously, reflect their own white Anglo-Saxon protestant values. Goals and standards which are culturally more appropriate and relevant for black and ethnic minority service users are likely to be hard for them to formulate. Service providers may, therefore, try to make inappropriate improvements to practices in their settings according to "white" standards, to the detriment of their black clients. Meanwhile, the number of black and ethnic minority service workers attending PASS workshops (where training in PASS is given) is very low (see Chapter 8, page 203.)

Challenging Racism

A further weakness in the principles of normalisation is the failure to help services to recognise and address the effects of racism on service users and service providers, even where the devaluation of black and ethnic minority people is acknowledged. Service providers must make a conscious effort, when seeking to pursue the principles of normalisation on behalf of black and ethnic minority people with learning difficulties, to challenge the oppressive effects of racism at the same time.

Normalisation and PASS are products of America in the early 1970s when many conscious and unconscious racist beliefs about racist and cultural superiority were only beginning to be challenged. However, these principles are still being disseminated and implemented in the UK today, in ways that do not take account of the life experiences of black and ethnic minority people. Not challenging racism in services is unacceptable in the Britain of the 1990s.

Normalisation can, and should be, a positive force for change in the lives of people with learning difficulties. But without more awareness of the dangers and limitations of these principles as they are currently interpreted and implemented, there is a real risk that their impact on black and ethnic minority people with learning difficulties may be a negative one.

Individual Programme Planning

People with learning difficulties usually have to rely on others to plan their lives. Individual programme planning has its origins in the movement to recognise that each person is unique and should receive assistance according to his or her individual needs, regardless of severity of handicap. Individual programme planning provides a systematic approach to support and care for people with learning difficulties designed to enable them to achieve short and longer term goals in their lives appropriate to their wishes, needs and circumstances. (For a basic introduction to IPPs, see Blunden et al, 1987.)

In our discussions with people with learning difficulties and their families and with service providers, we have identified a number of issues which need to be addressed before Individual Programme Plans can be assumed to be appropriate to the needs of a multiracial/multicultural society.

Working with Families

Individual Programme Plans focus heavily on the individual, taking far less account of his or her place in the dynamics of the family. In many ethnic minority communities the collective spirit of families and communities are more highly valued than the more self-centred individualism encouraged in white British society. For black and ethnic minority adults with learning difficulties, this difference in emphasis may be very important.

➢ Although services may recognise that adults with learning difficulties still need the support of their families, the model of "normal" family patterns and dynamics held by service providers is likely to be more appropriate to white families than those from black and ethnic minority communities.

➢ The idea of Training for Independence is one example of the way in which black and ethnic minority families may be alienated by services. The goals of training for independence identified within the IPP system (for example learning skills so that the individual may ultimately be able to live alone) can conflict with the tradition of extended family living which some black and ethnic minority families may prefer. White service providers are rarely skilled at (or confident about) working with families from black and ethnic minority communities whose norms, circumstances and experiences may differ significantly from their own.

Who Sets the Agenda ?

Individual Programme Plans are usually initiated by service providers to deal with issues or situations which they view as important or in need of discussion. The priorities and concerns of families and individuals are likely to be submerged in this service led approach. (A more egalitarian approach is the Shared Action Planning advocated by Brechin and Swain, 1987.)

Power Relationships

A fundamental premise of Individual Programme Plans is that service users, their families and service providers, should be involved on an equal basis. Such an equal partnership is, however, unlikely to be achieved given the unequal status between consumers and professionals, exacerbated by the status differentials between black and white people and the language and cultural differences which are seldom taken into account by existing services.

Unless conscious and practical efforts are made to redress these inequalities, the involvement of black families and individuals in the IPP system is in danger of being tokenist, their expected role being submissive acceptance and gratitude.

Communication Difficulties

Communication difficulties can greatly reduce the benefits of Individual Programme Plans for people with learning difficulties from black and ethnic minority communities. Key participants do not always appreciate the background and experiences of the service user and their relatives, or speak the same language. Interpreters are rarely made available. (Working through interpreters in situations involving detailed negotiations may be unsatisfactory anyway. A fuller discussion on the use of interpreters is given in Chapter 2.)

THE FOLESHILL MENTAL HANDICAP STUDY

An inter-agency team from Coventry Social Services conducted a study of the Foleshill area of the city. Their findings demonstrate the need for interpreters to be available to make home visits with service staff and be present at Individual Programme Plan or Review meetings. They cite the experience of one particular family:

Mr and Mrs Mishra never attended reviews at their daughter's day centre. In fact they had never visited there, and their only contact was by phone. Mr Mishra's command of English was not good, consequently he did not understand everything that was said. The family would have liked regular reports on Sushma's progress or to have had some assistance, via an interpreter, in understanding reviews.

(COCKING AND ATHWAL, 1990)

Conflicting Views

Service providers and service users may hold different ideas about appropriate directions for the future care of their family members. Conventions may differ in respect of what is appropriate to be discussed within and outside the family. The idea of talking about personal family matters and feelings and of discussing relatives with "strangers" may be unusual, if not unacceptable, for some people. There may also be differences about what can be discussed between men and women. For example, a man may feel it inappropriate or religiously improper for him to discuss the personal and intimate physical care of his adolescent daughter. He may feel embarrassed when relating to female service providers.

The situation can be aggravated by choice of venues/times for IPP meetings.

➢ Black and ethnic minority families, especially women and mothers with young children, may feel intimidated and isolated at the prospect of a meeting with a large number of white professionals in an environment in which they do not feel at ease. They may not, therefore, voice their concerns. Many black and ethnic minority people are used to, more comfortable with, and function more effectively on, a one to one basis on such matters. Indeed, most parents of any ethnic group would prefer such an approach.

➢ In these circumstances, there is a real risk that black and ethnic minority service users and their families may become merely passive recipients of plans and services alien to their wishes and needs.

Cultural Stereotyping

There has been recent interest in cultural information about black and ethnic minority people to inform the process of individual programme plans. This has not always worked to the advantage of black and ethnic minority people with learning difficulties for several reasons.

➢ Much of the existing literature has tended to promote the misconception of minority traditions and lifestyles as different, "backward" and "bizarre".

➢ Service providers often resort to cultural stereotypes and generalisations. For example, sweeping statements about what Sikhs, Hindus or Muslims think invariably ignore other factors such as social class, age and gender. This will be detrimental to the provision of good services for the individual service user.

➢ Preoccupations with culture often result in service providers attributing every problem to, and basing all decisions on, cultural differences. This "blaming the victim" approach diverts attention from underlying similarities in the needs of individual service users and their families for information, advice, support and sensitive and appropriate services.

The Role of Black Key Workers

Black and ethnic minority service providers often find themselves in circumstances where they assume the role of key person for people of their own ethnic origin with learning difficulties. They are expected to act as a voice outside the system whilst being part of that system — a position which may result in conflict with their managers. Not all black workers will be able to meet this challenge. It has to be recognised that this situation demands skills which are not always easily acquired. (The support needs of black staff are discussed in Chapter 7.)

When it comes to black service users, the white staff do not want to know. One minute I am classed as the expert and expected to sort out all their problems. The next I am told by managers that "I am taking it too far" and "overidentifying" with clients.

BLACK SERVICE PROVIDER AT THE SHARING EXPERIENCES CONFERENCE (BAXTER, 1990a)

ASSESSMENT

Assessment of the handicapped individual in such a way that assessment information is relevant to education and training is the cornerstone of effective intervention.

(HOGG AND MITTLER, 1980)

People with learning difficulties become passive objects of assessment. They play no active part in the process or have a say in what is being assessed.

(BRECHIN AND SWAIN, 1988)

A growing body of people are questioning the nature of assessment in the field of learning difficulties. There are concerns about the appropriateness of trying to test and measure a person's abilities by setting tasks which are administered by professionals, often in a strange situation within a set time (Pitt, 1987). There are major problems with traditional assessment methods, such as IQs. There is a danger of these tests being "done" to a person rather than by them or with them. They tend to give a static picture of the individual, highlighting inadequacies, defining what is lacking in social competence and skills rather than emphasising the positives. Initial negative labels of handicap or learning difficulty thus tend to be reinforced.

The inadequacies of assessment procedures become even more apparent when applied to black and ethnic minority children with learning difficulties. Such tests are based on the assumption that individuals will identify with images based on white middle class lifestyles and experiences. Racial stereotyping, inappropriate cultural approaches and language or communication difficulties further decrease the value of traditional assessments for black and ethnic minority children.

Cultural Bias

Assessment procedures are based on white British norms which may bear little relationship to the everyday life of the black or ethnic minority person and his/her family.

Unfamiliarity with test-taking procedures may result in the child being poorly motivated to carry out the test.

Unfamiliarity with testing equipment/instruments used may also produce inaccurate results. Two examples of this are:

➢ the use of stories which depict white suburban lifestyles

➢ the use of farm animals to test recognition when children are used only to an urban lifestyle

One test which used to be very popular asked children to say which of the following an umbrella was used to protect us from (rain, snow or sun). The Afro-Caribbean children, recalling their experience in the Caribbean, would of course say the sun. To the authorities the correct answer was, however, the rain. Our children were all then classed as not being very bright.

COMMUNITY RELATIONS OFFICER

One well known test has a picture of a couple involved in a Western style wedding ceremony. Hindu, Sikh and Muslim wedding ceremonies bear no resemblance to this. I know that Asian children would have difficulty recognising this one.

ASIAN CLINICAL PSYCHOLOGIST

The Health Visitor told me she was testing my baby's hearing. She began talking in a very high pitched voice and playing peek-a-boo with him. But he is only used to people's natural voices and we play different types of games. He was not interested and did not look at her. In fact Dapo was petrified. He had never seen so many white people before and they were all standing around looking at him. At the end of the test, they told me that they thought he was very deaf and would have to have further tests, but I know there was nothing wrong with his hearing — he could hear me coming a mile off.

AFRO-CARIBBEAN MOTHER

In our religion the pig and the dog are not considered nice animals. We find it very offensive when our children are tested on their ability to recognise a pink plastic pig. It is even worse when they are expected to show affection to dogs. It is against our religion. I just don't use them.

MUSLIM HEALTH VISITOR

Holistic Approaches to Assessment

New, more holistic, approaches to assessing people with learning difficulties are to be welcomed. Approaches such as *Getting to Know You* (Brost and Johnson, 1982) and *Shared Action Planning* (Brechin and Swain, 1987) aim to look at all aspects of an individual's life, placing the individual very much at the centre of the stage and trying to find out what their life has been like in the past, is at the present and could be in the future. A specific aim is to shift power from professionals to the individuals themselves by involving them in their own assessment.

For Brechin and Swain (1988) assessment is:

A continuing process of discussion, shared experiences, observation and negotiation between the individual, key people, and also others such as professionals, who may be able to communicate relevant and useful information and suggestions.

Thus the focus is on building up a whole picture of the person. The dynamic nature of their lives has to be acknowledged. Emphasis has to be placed on the individual speaking up for him or herself wherever possible, facilitating satisfying lifestyles and relationships (Pitt, 1987).

These changes in assessment must take into consideration the specific needs of black and ethnic minority people with learning difficulties. It has to be recognised that their position may be doubly disadvantaged. Thus effort has to be made to ensure that:

➢ attention is paid to paragraph 70 of the DES Circular 1/83 which states that "a child should not be taken to have a learning difficulty because the language or form of language of his home is different from the language of instruction in his school"

➢ interpreters are used where people's mother tongue is not English

➢ all procedures are looked at critically for cultural bias and stereotypes

➢ the part that racism plays in black and ethnic minority people's lives and how this can affect achievement is recognised and taken into consideration during assessment

➢ bilingual children, or children who do not speak English, have the opportunity to express themselves in their home language

➢ new and more flexible approaches are developed, particularly ways of involving parents (see Chapter 4)

Debates about standard assessment procedures have been in progress for many years. The adverse effects on black and ethnic minority people are only slowly being acknowledged. More urgent response to these concerns is necessary to prevent negative and far reaching consequences on the lives of black and ethnic minority people with learning difficulties.

REFERENCES

Bank-Mikkelson N E (1969): *Changing Patterns in Residential Services for the Mentally Retarded.* Washington DC, President's Committee on Mental Retardation.

Baxter C (1990a): *Sharing Experiences to Challenge Assumptions. A Report of Two Workshops Around Services for Black People with Learning Difficulties.* London, CCETSW. Forthcoming.

Blunden R, Evans G and Humphreys S (1987): *Planning with Individuals: An Outline Guide.* Cardiff, Mental Handicap in Wales, Applied Research Unit.

Brechin A and Swain J (1987): *Changing Relationships. Shared Action Planning with People with a Mental Handicap.* London, Harper and Row.

Brechin A and Swain J (1988): "A share of the action for consumers". *Community Living,* March/April, pp 20–21.

Brost M and Johnson T (1982): *Getting to Know You: One Approach to Service Assessment and Planning for Individuals with Disabilities.* Wisconsin, Wisconsin Coalition for Advocacy.

Caring for People: Community Care in the Next Decade and Beyond (1989). London, HMSO.

Cocking I and Athwal S (1990): "A special case for special treatment". *Social Work Today,* 8 February, pp 12–13.

DES Circular 1/83: *Assessment and Statements of Special Educational Needs.*

Dungate M (1984): *A Multiracial Society. The Role of National Voluntary Organisations.* London, Bedford Square Press.

Dutt R (1989) (ed): *Community Care. Race Dimension.* London, NISW, Race Equality Unit.

Griffiths R/DHSS (1988): *Community Care: Agenda for Action.* London, HMSO.

Hogg J and Mittler P (1980): "Recent research in mental handicap: Issues and perspectives". In Hogg J and Mittler P (eds): *Advances in Mental Handicap Research,* Vol 1. Chichester, John Wiley and Sons.

Nirje B (1970): "The normalisation principle — Implications and comments". *British Journal of Mental Subnormality,* 16, pp 62–70.

Open University (1986): *Mental Handicap: Patterns for Living* (Course P555). Book One, "Living and Learning". Milton Keynes, Open University.

Pitt M (1987): "Client choice and self determination". *Care in the Community Newsletter,* Autumn, No 7, pp 7–9.

Race D (1987): "Normalisation: Theory and practice". In Malin N (ed): *Reassessing Community Care.* London, Croom Helm.

Wolfensberger W (1983): "Social role valorisation: A proposed new term for the principle of normalisation". *Mental Retardation,* December, pp 234–9.

Wolfensberger W and Glenn L (1975): *PASS 3. Program Analysis of Service Systems — A Method for the Quantitative Evaluation of Human Services.* Toronto, National Institute on Mental Retardation, 3rd edition.

Wolfensberger W and Thomas S (1983): *Program Analysis of Service Systems: Implementation of Normalisation Goals (PASSING).* Toronto, National Institute of Mental Retardation.

FURTHER READING

Connelly N (1988): *Care in a Multiracial Community.* London, Policy Studies Institute.

RESOURCES

Contracts for Care: Issues for Black and Other Ethnic Minority Voluntary Groups (1990) — An information pack dealing with the general issues around contracting with particular reference to the black voluntary sector, and the practical issues to be overcome. Price £5. Single copies free to local voluntary organisations.

From: Community Care Project
             NCVO, 26 Bedford Square
             London WC1B 3HU
             Tel: 071 636 4066

THE FIRST YEARS

From the day she was born, I had a feeling that something was not quite right. Baby was two years old, however, before I found out what was wrong. The Health Visitor was talking to my neighbour who spoke English. (I did not speak English at the time.) She picked up from the health visitor that my daughter was mentally handicapped. She, of course, mentioned this to me because she was surprised that I had kept it from her. As you can realise, I was very shocked.

ASIAN MOTHER

INTRODUCTION

Having a handicapped baby can be devastating for anyone. In this chapter we look at what support and help black and ethnic minority families need.

➢ Prevalence
➢ Antenatal Services
➢ Breaking the News and Counselling
➢ The Needs of Carers
➢ Interpreters
➢ Fostering and Adoption
➢ Take Up of Benefits

Several of the issues addressed in this chapter are also relevant to other age groups, but may be first encountered by parents in the early years. In particular, the question of support for carers is addressed in several chapters.

PREVALENCE

There is no national information on the prevalence of learning difficulties amongst black and ethnic minority communities. Local studies, however, have provided some useful information.

One main area of concern has been that the prevalence of learning difficulties among black and ethnic minority children appears to be higher than among white children. Information from some of the Northern mill towns is particularly revealing. In Rochdale, for example, although only 5.5% of the population are Asian, they make up 40% of all the children attending the Development Therapy Unit and 35% of the children receiving portage (Whitfield, 1988). A Manchester study revealed more of each type of severe disability (Akinsola and Fryers, 1986). In Oldham, Asian babies make up 18% of the births, yet over a third of the under fives (double the expected rate) have severe learning difficulties (BASW, 1987). Another study in Camberwell demonstrated that children with severe language impairment were significantly over-represented among children born to parents from the New Commonwealth (Wing, 1969).

There has been a long-running debate about the cause of the apparently higher prevalence of learning difficulties in some minority ethnic communities. Those factors which have been suggested as specifically relevant are a higher incidence of congenital rubella syndrome, and a higher frequency of first cousin marriages.

➢ The incidence of **congenital rubella** has been identified as two to three times higher in Asian than non-Asian births in England and Wales (Miller et al, 1987). There may be two reasons for this. Firstly, rubella immunisation rates may be low among Asian girls at school in the UK, if information about the immunisation, and the need to return consent forms is not translated or interpreted. It is interesting to note here that immunisation take-up in Bradford among Asian infants was higher than among non- Asians, perhaps because they were given during routine baby clinic visits (Baker et al, 1984). Secondly, the relatively few numbers of young Asian women who come to Britain after the age of routine rubella immunisation in schools may be susceptible to infection if they have not been exposed to rubella in their country of origin. A similar situation pertained for Afro-Caribbean women coming to Britain in the 1960s.

➤ The issue of **first cousin marriages** is far more emotive and controversial and has contributed much to an approach which "blames the victim" (see page 36). First cousin marriages may increase the risk of autosomal recessive conditions, but many of these conditions are so rare that 50% consanguinity would be required before significant numbers would appear in the population. Furthermore, in the few studies which have carefully explored the association between consanguinity and the incidence of congenital malformations, a significantly high correlation has not been established (Rao and Inbaraj, 1980; Terry et al, 1985; Rosenthal et al, 1988; Kumar, 1990; Pearson, 1990).

It seems to be clear that congenital rubella syndrome and first cousin marriages cannot completely explain the relatively higher than expected proportion of black and ethnic minority infants with learning difficulties. Other explanations must be explored.

Poverty

Most congenital abnormalities, including learning impairments, have causes present in the preconceptual period, at the time of conception and during the early weeks of pregnancy. This will include the effects of poor housing, environmental pollution, inadequate and inappropriate education and other factors associated with material deprivation which have an indirect effect on pregnancy outcome. Black and ethnic minority communities have lower incomes than the white community (Brown, 1984), and the correlation between poverty and perinatal mortality is well established (Townsend et al, 1988). In areas with high rates of mental handicap, there are also high perinatal mortality rates. There is also substantial evidence that perinatal mortality and morbidity rates are higher among those babies whose mothers were born in the New Commonwealth and Pakistan (Balarajan and Botting, 1989).

Antenatal Services

Maternity services are known to influence pregnancy outcome. Several studies have identified a problem of racial inequality in access to antenatal services. A study in Leicester showed that only 64% of Asian mothers had over five months of antenatal care (Clarke and Clayton, 1983). Similar findings were demonstrated in a Bradford study in which 60% of Asian mothers, as compared with 20% of their non-Asian counterparts, had less than four months antenatal care (Lumb et al, 1981). Other studies have highlighted the low uptake of maternity services by Afro-Caribbean women (Larbie, 1984). The main reason for underuse of services is their culturally inappropriate and unwelcoming nature (Pearson, 1985).

Diagnosis of certain abnormalities at between 8 and 16 weeks of pregnancy is a routine part of antenatal care. Counselling during this period is of particular importance, so that prospective parents have the opportunity to discuss any particular genetic risks and make informed decisions regarding their pregnancy. Preconceptual and antenatal genetic counselling, however, is almost unheard of among black and ethnic minority families. Where genetic counselling has been established in minority communities, it has been principally for specific blood disorders, sickle cell anaemia and thalassaemia. The skills and the expertise necessary for sensitive and effective work with black and ethnic minority families are gravely lacking in the health services. (See section on genetic counselling, page 36.)

Mohinder and Pargan Singh are well into middle age and are not first cousins. Of their five grown up children, three are handicapped. The couple are dedicated Sikhs and devoted parents. I asked them whether, if they had known that they stood a good chance of having more handicapped children after their first, it would have altered the size of family they chose to have. Astonished, they both asked if one could tell whether a child would be handicapped and said that had they been aware of the risk, they would have sought medical advice.

(Borum, 1987)

Linkworkers

There are a growing number of local initiatives throughout the country which aim to improve the access and quality of services for black and ethnic minority women during the prenatal, antenatal and postnatal period. They are based mainly on the concepts of advocacy and outreach using "linkworkers". The roles of linkworkers and (patient) advocates are similar. Precise duties depend on local management structures and particular emphases within district health authorities. Linkworkers are more than just interpreters. They are active facilitators between health professionals and their clients, bridging barriers, interpreting (both verbally and non-verbally) and attempting to allay anxieties. The number of linkworker projects has increased over the years. Two examples are described on pages 31 and 32.

IDEAS IN PRACTICE

Multi-Ethnic Women's Health Project — City and Hackney

Hackney has a large black and ethnic minority community mainly from the Caribbean with a smaller proportion from the Indian subcontinent, Turkey and Cyprus. Unemployment is high and poverty widespread. The non-English speaking women are in a particularly vulnerable position, facing severe social problems, especially in dealing with authorities, such as the NHS, which have not responded adequately to the local multiracial population.

In 1979, the City and Hackney Community Health Council called a meeting to discuss what could be done to:

➤ improve the physical health of non-English speaking women and babies in the community

➤ develop a support system for them and hence help their mental health

➤ reduce racial tension in the hospital

➤ help the hospital staff to understand the needs of ethnic minority women

Discussions were held with Hackney Council for Racial Equality, health authority officers and nursing and medical staff at the local maternity unit. The outcome was the Hackney Multi-Ethnic Women's Health Project, the objectives of which are to:

➤ improve access to the health service for non-English speaking women during pregnancy, childbirth and the postnatal period

➤ help women understand the choices open to them so that they can make informed decisions about their own health

➤ advise the health authority on policy and practice concerning the needs of non-English speaking women

➤ help and encourage health service staff to provide a service to this high risk group

The project employs staff from different local communities on a full and part-time basis to support minority women using the health services. They are selected for their personal qualities, and are women with strong community links who have children of their own and have had experience of using the NHS. They thus share many experiences with the women with whom they work.

The staff work principally in antenatal and postnatal care. Although their duties include interpreting, their role is essentially that of an advocate who makes sure that the women are aware of their rights and understand the implications of medical care. They speak Turkish, Gujerati, Bengali, Urdu, Hindi in addition to English.

The emphasis in the project is on changing NHS structures to make the service more sensitive to the needs of users, and developing client-led policies. This necessitates building close working relationships with the NHS at district level and at service level, and extending the knowledge and contacts into the community. It is important in developing close links that the project and its workers remain independent from the NHS hierarchy.

The project is funded by Hackney and Islington Inner City Partnership monies through the District Health Authority's partnership programme. In April 1989 the project was taken on as a part of mainstream service provision by the Health Authority.

Contact: Hafiz Ece, Co-ordinator
Linkworkers Project
City and Hackney Community
   Health Council
210 Kingsland Road
London E2 8EB

Tel: 071 739 6308/8357
Or: 071 729 7285

IDEAS IN PRACTICE

Linkworkers Project — Haringey

The objectives of the Haringey Linkworkers Project are to offer support and provide health information to black and ethnic minority women on health issues, especially antenatal and postnatal care. Thirteen linkworkers and a co-ordinator include Turkish, Greek, Afro-Caribbean, Asian and Chinese women.

The project operates mainly from the North Middlesex Hospital in Haringey. A large proportion of the project's work involves working with health staff in the maternity and postnatal units. This includes communicating information from doctor to client and vice versa. The linkworkers also work in the community at an antenatal clinic which offers a more locally based service and continuity of care.

The most important aspect of the linkworkers project is to offer advice and support to black and ethnic minority women using the maternity services. This includes facilitating communication between users and health workers, particularly where the client is a non-English speaker. As the project has developed, the scope of the work has moved beyond the hospital. The project advises women and their families on welfare rights, housing and other community issues. Initial contact with the women is made through antenatal and child health clinics where the linkworkers are based. The project also receives telephone referrals from the hospital and the community based health services.

The linkworkers are given an induction course prior to starting to work with pregnant women, covering the issues involved in providing health care in a multiracial society. In addition, there is regular training on subjects such as counselling, welfare rights and maternity benefits.

The initial funding came from the Manpower Services Commission Agency for Community Programmes with support from the Haringey Community Health Council, but the project is now a part of the mainstream health services of the North Middlesex Hospital.

The project has a support group consisting of a sister from the antenatal unit, a district midwife, a health visitor, the secretary of Haringey Community Health Council and community representatives.

Contact:　Glenda Kirwan, Manager
　　　　　　Linkworkers Department
　　　　　　Haringey Health Authority
　　　　　　Montford House
　　　　　　The Green
　　　　　　London N15 4AN

　　　　　　Tel:　081 808 1081 ext 215

BREAKING THE NEWS AND COUNSELLING

There is no "good" way of telling parents their child is mentally handicapped, but there must be ways of not making a bad situation worse, and of not adding to the suffering that is already bound to be considerable.

(HANNAM, 1980)

The Open University course *Mental Handicap: Patterns for Living* (Book 2, "Changes and Choices") suggests the following guidelines for breaking the news.

➢ Parents should be told as soon as possible.

➢ Parents should be told together.

➢ The baby should be present, if possible. This helps parents feel that their child is valued.

➢ The discussion should be private.

➢ The news giver should be a well-informed person (for example, the paediatrician concerned).

➢ The news giver should explain the facts as simply as possible and not try to influence decision making.

➢ A subsequent interview should be arranged so that parents can ask questions and seek practical information and advice.

➢ Follow-up at home should be arranged with a "key worker", usually a health visitor, general practitioner or social worker, who can offer continuing support and practical information and advice.

Experience shows that if the family is from a black or ethnic minority community, these standards are less likely to be achieved. One Asian mother told us:

When my baby was born, there were no professional staff around who could speak my language. Eventually staff identified a cleaner who could speak to me working on the ward. The cleaner was asked to break the news to me.

One of the biggest problems in achieving these standards will be if parents and professionals do not speak a common language. Sometimes an interpreter or an advocate will be essential to ensure that the news is broken in the most sensitive and acceptable way.

In some cases, parents may be the first to recognise that their child has a learning difficulty, particularly if the disabilities are not evident at birth. It is important that they are listened to and given the respect and credit due to them as parents who know their child best. There is also a need to be vigilant that we do not have different expectations of developmental progress for black and ethnic minority children, as compared with white children. An Afro-Caribbean mother who was also a health visitor told us of her experiences:

It was I who brought it to their attention. When my son was about five years old, I knew there was something wrong with him. He was not developing normally. His pincer grasp was not very good. I kept telling them but they kept saying he was alright, and that it was only because I had some knowledge and that I was an overanxious mother … I kept telling them something was wrong, but they told me that my expectations were raised now that I am in this country and that he was quite normal, and my expectations of him were unrealistic … Another time the explanation they gave me was that it was because he had difficulty adjusting to British society. They said he would soon adjust to the culture and settle down. We did not know what adjusting they were talking about. My son was born here and he was only five at the time … It was years before they came to agree with me and to give my son the services he needed.

Medical Explanations

There may be a need for some medical explanation of the child's condition. It is important to find out what the family already understands and their beliefs and views about possible causes. Where parents' understanding may not have a Western medical scientific base, it should not simply be dismissed. Rather it should be built upon. An Afro-Caribbean mother whom we interviewed said this of her son:

He was quite alright until he suffered two shocks. Firstly, I cut his hair while he was still too young. Then one day my husband and I had a heated argument in front of him. We were very cross with each other and this upset him. He never recovered from it … They tell me he was born like that but it is not so. That made me feel so bad.

In most cultures there is a stigma attached to people with learning difficulties. (Britain is, of course, no exception.) For people with strong traditional religious beliefs, there may be a sense of human or divine retribution or punishment for the family's sins. Some cultures have also viewed people with learning difficulties as "a gift from God" or in some way "divine".

The following views of a social worker are based on her experience in Keighley where she had specific responsibilities for ethnic minority families. **It is important to point out here that these factors will not necessarily be relevant to all families. Cultural stereotyping must be avoided.**

While not rejecting the child, many parents have difficulty in accepting the permanent nature of the handicap, and continue to hope that there will be a cure.

This hope for a cure partly explains the difficulty in understanding the purpose of available therapy. Parents may go from one doctor to another and then to Hakims in search of the ultimate treatment. If the child is hospitalised, there is often the expectation of a rapid recovery. In the absence of obvious response to treatment, the exercise or medicine may be stopped, in the belief that it has failed.

(PEARSON, 1982)

Emotional Support

Parents need a lot of emotional support to work through their reactions to the discovery of their child's handicap. The opportunity to express grief, anger, guilt and fear are crucial to their final acceptance of the handicapped child within the family. These reactions are common to any parent discovering their child has a learning difficulty. They may manifest themselves in culturally different ways. The underlying human feelings and emotions, however, remain the same. Those involved with black and ethnic minority families will, therefore, need to be aware of the phases and stages through which the family is passing, and will need to recognise their own limitations. At times it may be necessary to ask for help from others.

There is evidence that black and ethnic minority families do not always get the support they need in this area.

There is this Asian father who, after three years, is still convinced that his daughter's mental handicap was the result of brain damage during delivery. Since her birth, he has been trying to sue the health authority. He has spent a lot of time and energy going from one place to the next in the hope that someone can help him. He has been to see me on several occasions and has also been to the Community Health Council and the Citizens Advice Bureau. Everyone feels that he is simply aggressive. It is obvious that he is still at the denial stage and has not had much time spent with him. He is not receiving the counselling and support necessary to see him through this bad period. After three years, Mr X is still very angry and has become a very frustrated and almost demented man.

ASIAN SOCIAL WORKER

Genetic Counselling

Where there is believed to be a genetic component to the handicap, families may be offered genetic counselling to enable them to make an informed choice about future children.

One obstacle to appropriate genetic counselling services for black and ethnic minority families is the lack of adequate communication resulting from language and cultural differences. Another important issue is whether the particular methods used in the counselling process are appropriate. For example, can all families relate to the flow chart tree method which is usually used to explain genetic inheritance? Most parents will find the concepts involved in genetic counselling difficult to understand. The concept of an autosomal recessive condition — where non-handicapped parents can produce children with a handicap — is one which is likely to baffle the ordinary person who has had no scientific training.

Of more concern is the prevalence of the popularly held belief — even amongst some professionals — that the cause of the apparent excess of Asian children with learning difficulties has been first cousin marriages.

Frequently we come across examples where a couple or family as a whole are made to feel guilty because it has been suggested to them that the custom of cousin marriages is the sole cause of their child's disability, which might in fact be due to a non-genetic factor such as an intra-uterine infection or secondary perinatal complication.

SPECIALIST DOCTOR IN GENETICS

As part of my training I had a lecture from a specialist genetic counsellor. She tended to cite only cases of arranged and first cousin marriages. Their feelings often come over even if they try to hide it under some sort of professional cover … Where I work the staff just assume all the Asian children are this way because their parents marry their cousins. They talk about this quite openly and even discuss it with other parents. They like the sensationalism — The Sun reader, headline approach. They enjoy it and spread it. They do not realise how much power they have.

AFRO-CARIBBEAN COMMUNITY MENTAL HANDICAP TEAM NURSE

Clearly, this kind of misinformation, personal prejudice and stereotyping will affect professional practice adversely. It is easy to understand that families can be alienated by services which reflect these attitudes.

This could probably account for the numbers who do not wish to be referred for genetic counselling, particularly the younger girls who grew up here. They have already sussed out how we feel. They are aware of our disapproval of cousin marriages. They know it is frowned upon … A lot of the time they get very upset about being asked for so much information about their family.

HEALTH VISITOR, GENETIC COUNSELLING

- In cousin marriages where there are autosomal recessive conditions, it is important that staff should not blame the couples, but put the emphasis on helping the families to appreciate the increased risk involved.

➢ Where it is thought that termination of pregnancy would be offensive to couples, this option should be handled with caution, couples being allowed to identify and explore this course of action for themselves.

IDEAS IN PRACTICE

Some health authorities and community organisations have established counselling and screening programmes for sickle cell anaemia and thalassaemia. These are autosomal recessively inherited blood disorders which have a higher prevalence among black and ethnic minority people than among white people. Staff employed in the projects are usually of the same ethnic background as the population affected by the disorder.

Interracial / Crosscultural Counselling

The importance of crosscultural counselling in the UK has only recently begun to be discussed. There is very little research or information in Britain on matching clients and counsellors on the basis of ethnic origin or sex. Information which is available suggests the following.

➢ Counselling in a formal sense may be new to many black and ethnic minority people. It is important that the counsellor's role and expectations are made clear and that the family is given the opportunity to clarify their expectations and understanding of what they hope to receive from the relationship.

➢ Many black and ethnic minority families may have had negative experiences of white organisations. They may already be nursing guilt as a result of insensitive genetic counselling or thoughtless comments by staff. They may experience feelings of anxiety, discomfort, a lack of trust and confidence which may result in a reluctance to accept help from, or confide in, a white counsellor. Crosscultural counselling can only be successful when counsellors are aware of their own attitudes, personal expectations, values and prejudices and how these affect their behaviour.

> Choice is largely precluded by the lack of black counsellors in the health and social services or voluntary agencies. Situations in which white counsellors simply offload their black and ethnic minority clients to their few black colleagues must be avoided. White counsellors must be encouraged and trained to offer sensitive and appropriate services themselves to all clients.

> Some women may be unable to benefit from the services of a male counsellor. Such situations will need to be thoughtfully discussed and suitable alternatives arranged.

> It is important that families and individuals are seen as a whole and not in isolation from their life experiences and communities. Counsellors must demonstrate an appreciation of the disadvantaged position of black and ethnic minority people in our society and convey an understanding of these experiences.

> In situations where there are close community networks, families will need to be reassured of complete confidentiality when allocated a counsellor of the same ethnic origin.

Peer Parents

A survey by Harlesden Community Mental Handicap Team revealed that Asian and Afro-Caribbean parents of children with learning difficulties wanted to meet others with similar experiences, but did not have opportunities to do so (Open University, 1990). The involvement of peer parents in breaking the news, and in counselling, is growing in popularity. Black and ethnic minority families will also benefit from this approach, but it is important that families' views and wishes are identified and respected. In close-knit communities, there may be a particular need to ensure that anonymity and confidentiality are protected.

The Needs of Carers

Ethnic minority women experience the same problems as other women providing care for dependent family members. However, there are many ways in which their difficulties are made greater by a society which does not recognise their special needs. In addition to pressures of institutional racism in service delivery, racism in employment, in education, in housing, there may be particular cultural and domestic demands that exacerbate the problem.

(Quoted in Contact a Family, 1989a)

Like the white community, most black and ethnic minority people will wish to care for their relatives themselves. It is, therefore, important to ensure that families have the necessary support to do this. From our discussions with carers, we conclude that the needs of black carers have been overlooked for the following reasons.

➤ **Ill-founded assumptions** — There is a commonly held view that black and ethnic minority people have self-supporting family networks and prefer to look after their own.

➤ **Lack of information** — Black and ethnic minority families may find it difficult to gain access to the complicated health and welfare systems. Many will not know how they work. Since very little relevant material is translated, access to information about benefits and alternative forms of care (and skills) usually depends on the ability to read and speak English. A lot of time and effort may, therefore, be spent by some families before they find out about benefits and services to which they are entitled.

DISABLED PERSONS ACT, 1986

The 1986 Disabled Persons (Services, Consultation and Representation) Act reinforces and extends the duties of local authorities to meet various needs of disabled people and gives disabled people additional rights of representation. So far, only some sections of the Act have been implemented:

Section 4, the duty to assess the need for services

Sections 5 and 6, the identification and assessment of disabled school-leavers

Section 8 (1), the duty to take carers' abilities into account

Section 9, the duty to provide information about services

Section 10, the duty to consult with organisations of disabled people when making co-options onto committees

A report by the Social Services Inspectorate (based on an inspection by them of 1 in 3 social services departments in England between March and June 1989) was highly critical of the generally slow progress in implementing the Act (Warburton, 1990a).

William Warburton, author of the report, commented:

There is cause for concern in that little information about services was made available to people for whom English was not the first language, and much training did not address the needs of minority groups.

(WARBURTON, 1990b)

➤ **Lack of training** — Carers are often not taught the practical skills which could make their work easier and help their relative to develop more independence.

➤ **Inappropriate services** — Services do not take into account the needs of black and ethnic minority carers. Families may not find the particular services available useful or feel welcome to use them. Respite care is a case in point. Many families would prefer to see their relatives placed in situations where their individual cultural, religious and physical needs will be met and where their differing needs are not seen as a problem.

We need the break very much but there are men working in that place. She is of the age now where we would not want her to be looked after by a man. It is part of our religion. How can you tell them all this?
ASIAN MOTHER

We do not like the children to have any meat, in case it is not halal. As far as bathing is concerned, we would prefer the girls to be washed and dressed by women but we have now got used to the boy being dressed by women.
ASIAN MOTHER

In one area we visited we were aware that respite care was rarely used by Asian families. One issue is how respite is defined. Service providers may assume that the maximum support needed is for a parent or carer to go on a fortnight's holiday. A need to return to Pakistan to attend a funeral or other important family occasion, perhaps over a longer period, therefore, poses difficulties. Such criteria need to be reviewed so that there is greater flexibility to meet the needs of individual families. (For a more detailed review of the issues surrounding respite care, see Chapter 4.)

➤ **Racism** — Many carers are aware of the prevalent view of black and ethnic minority people as scroungers. They will be anxious about putting themselves in situations in which they may be discriminated against by some staff and treated with hostility. One Asian mother had this to say about the home care aide provided by the local health authority:

You could tell by her face that she did not like coming to our house. She treated my husband like a child and resented him sleeping in the day, although he worked a night shift.

➤ **Reluctance to apply for benefits** — Many black and ethnic minority carers still need to be convinced that it is acceptable to receive financial help like benefits. Others feel it would be frowned upon in their communities if they sought alternative forms of care outside the boundaries of family and relatives.

➤ **Young carers** — Carers from black and ethnic minority communities may be substantially younger than their white counterparts. They may assume this role at the expense of a career which could

IDEAS IN PRACTICE

Black and Ethnic Minority Carers' Forum

The King's Fund Centre has a Black and Ethnic Minority Carers Forum. A development officer (black and ethnic minority carers) has been appointed to work with other organisations on information and education projects to help carers and professionals. Service development projects are also planned which will aim to improve the delivery of community services to meet carers' needs.

By mid 1989 funding was provided to four agencies which focused on the needs of black and ethnic minority carers:

➤ Voluntary Action Leicester, in collaboration with SCOPE (an Asian community organisation), to provide a video in Hindi and booklets in four Asian languages for carers in the Leicester area (English versions also available)

➤ the Birmingham Community Care Special Action Project, to develop guidelines on how black and ethnic minority carers can be consulted more effectively and their views fed into the planning and delivery of services

➤ the National Self-Help Support Centre, to provide grants for black and ethnic minority self-help carers' groups undertaking information and education activities

➤ the Standing Conference of Ethnic Minority Senior Citizens (SCEMSC), to research the needs of minority ethnic carers in Southwark

Contact: Janice Robinson
          Carers Unit
          King's Fund Centre
          126 Albert Street
          London NW1 7NF

          Tel: 071 267 6111

significantly affect their future lives. An 18 year old Muslim girl who has personally chosen to help her mother care for three siblings with learning difficulties had this to say:

Sometimes I think about how I would like to find a job and have a different life. But then if I am working, I would always be worrying about what was happening at home. My older sister stayed home to do this until she got married. Now I am doing it. I sometimes look at my little sister and think, "When I get married, it will be her turn to do this".

Ideas In Practice

Asian Carers Group

This is a support group for Asian families who have a member who has a mental or physical handicap. The aim is to enable parents to share problems and ideas. This group was initiated in 1988 by Consultant Paediatrician Dr Shirley Lewis, a Registrar, Dr Neera Ghaziuddin, hospital based Social Worker, Virinda Basi, with support from the Community Nursing Team and Community Mental Handicap Team.

Contact: Shamim Sagar
            Asian Carers Group
            Vale Brook House
            City Hospital
            Hucknall Road
            Nottingham
            Tel: 0602 691169 ext 45056

Or: Kathy Taylor
            Nottinghamshire County
                Council
            Ashbourne House
            49–51 Forest Road East
            Nottingham NG1 4HT
            Tel: 0602 413707

Ideas In Practice

Birmingham Community Care Special Action ? Support Needs of Carers in Black and Ethnic M Communities

The Birmingham Community Care Special Action P? (CCSAP) was established at the beginning of 1987 w? principal objectives:

➤ to establish the means by which people with speci? could make wider use of the range of ordinary fac? a city wide basis

➤ to establish mechanisms by which the views and experiences of service users could systematically in? the planning and development of services

Black and ethnic minority needs have been a high pri? the project. The two major areas of work with minori? communities have been:

➤ to improve support for informal carers

➤ to identify more satisfactory approaches to daytim? occupations for black and ethnic minority people learning difficulties

Consultation meetings have been held with carers. Interpreters were made available and in many instance? publicity material was translated.

their moderate success it was felt that
meetings were not the most appropriate
consult with black and ethnic minority
The Community Care Special Action
opened discussions with a number of
ity workers and community
tatives, particularly in various Asian
-Caribbean communities. It was
d that much more use should be made
unity groups, local churches and
local press, newspapers and radio
especially those in black and ethnic
communities. It was also suggested
public meetings undertaken by the
should be on a much more local
vering just a few streets, with meetings
e's houses rather than public venues.
SAP, therefore, obtained a grant from
g's Fund to undertake a specific short
quiry into the needs of black and
inority carers. The project aimed to:

tify different ways of reaching carers in
ic minority communities, particularly
initially) carers from Afro-Caribbean
munities living in West Birmingham
rict (including Handsworth)

hods might include working with
munity groups, local churches and
ples, local press and radio stations
ch cater for black and ethnic minority
munities. Almost certainly, this would
lve working on a more local level.

sult with carers in ethnic minority
munities about their experiences and
ds, and the changes to existing services
nake them more acceptable which *they*
sidered were required

➤ compare support needs described by white
carers with those in other minority
communities, to improve understanding of
common experiences and differences

➤ compile detailed proposals for specific
action to be taken by Birmingham City
Council

➤ link carers consulted with existing
networks and explore ways of developing
new ones

➤ produce guidelines for use by other
statutory authorities, which would give
practical guidance on the development of
consultation with carers in black and
ethnic minority communities

The guidelines would seek to illustrate the
benefits of different methods of
consultation and to identify the limitations
of different approaches as they became
clear.

➤ produce and implement a strategy to
disseminate the guidelines to relevant
authorities and agencies including black
and ethnic minority organisations

For details of the final report, contact:

Adrienne Jones, Director
Birmingham Social Services
Department
Community Care Performance
Review Group
Snow Hill House
10–15 Livesey Street
Birmingham B3 2PE
Tel: 021 235 3567

INTERPRETERS

Many black and ethnic minority families speak
excellent English in addition to their
competence in several other languages. Others
may speak little or no English at all. The
majority of services in Britain are provided in
English only. Language differences may,
therefore, restrict some black and ethnic
minority people's access to the services they
require.

Poor communication can have serious
consequences. It can, for example, result in
misdiagnosis by health service staff,
inappropriate assessment and intervention by
social services, and non-receipt of welfare and
benefit entitlements. Poor communication also
wastes time and leads to frustration and poor
job satisfaction. Ad hoc attempts to
communicate across language differences are
common in our health and social welfare
system. The use of signs or gestures, children
and other relatives or bilingual strangers are
ineffective and sometimes dangerous practices.

A growing number of agencies acknowledge
that they discriminate by providing services
only in English. Increasingly, interpreters are
employed to improve services for non-English
speakers, but where they are used on an ad hoc
basis the situation is far from satisfactory.

➤ Interpreters are often employed as Section 11 workers on very low
   grades and on a short term basis only. (See Chapter 7, page 178, for
   more on Section 11 funding.)

➤ Many are dissatisfied with their role.

➤ Interpreters are rarely rewarded adequately for their work. They feel
   neither recognised nor valued, and have little training or support.
   The absence of these essentials will undoubtedly affect the quality of
   their work.

Working with an Interpreter — Qualities and Skills Needed

Interpreter

➤ Patient — particularly when working with poor and reluctant communicators

➤ Fluent in both languages as well as dialect

➤ Good at listening to both sides

➤ Non-judgemental and value free

➤ Able to hold discussions with health worker

➤ Avoids putting own interpretations

➤ Emotionally strong

➤ Confident

➤ Able to cope with stress

➤ Understands workings and procedures of the health services, social services and education agencies involved

➤ Knows when to ask for help

Service Provider

➤ Respects the interpreter

➤ Does not feel he/she has a monopoly on knowledge or skills

➤ Able to allow patient and interpreter to speak in their own language and not be suspicious

➤ Able to listen carefully to the interpreter

➤ If in doubt is able to intervene tactfully and find out what is being said

➤ Briefs interpreter beforehand and expresses concerns later

➤ Pauses a lot and allows plenty of time

➤ Takes note of odd sounding responses

➤ Uses clear expression — not slang or jargon

➤ Uses extra resources and diagrams

(ADAPTED FROM LARBIE ET AL, 1987)

If an interpreter programme is to be effective it is important that the implications for employment and training of interpreters are anticipated and that the staff who will be working with them are trained to do so sensitively and effectively.

Gender, religion, class and age can affect the perspective and interpretations of the parties involved. For example, some clients may find it difficult to speak freely about intimate matters with members of the opposite sex. Similarly, intergenerational differences and their impact on childrearing may be a particularly sensitive area. **It is essential that an interpreter can establish credibility with his/her client. Matching interpreters and clients is vital.**

Fostering and Adoption

Most black and ethnic minority children with learning difficulties will live at home with their families. Some, however, are likely to be taken into local authority care. For a variety of reasons, including the relatively young age of the black and ethnic minority population, there are disproportionate numbers of black and ethnic minority children in care, in residential homes or waiting to be fostered or adopted.

Children with learning difficulties from any background who have been fostered or adopted have not had much opportunity to speak for themselves about their experiences. We can, however, learn much about this from others, who may find it easier to express themselves and share the same experience of being black and brought up in white families or environments.

We quote from *Black and In Care* (BCSG, 1984), a report of a workshop for black children and adults who had been in care. They identified the following issues which affected their everyday lives and put forward recommendations as follows:

All children were treated the same — that is, we all had a white image projected on us …

Young people should be aware of their culture and be prepared for the racism they are going to face in the community. The best people to make these decisions would be black people as they would have faced these problems and learnt to cope with them.

The black child needs to be somewhere where there are some black people or other families who they can identify with.

Foster parents didn't seem to understand that the majority of black kids have dry skins and, therefore, need a good moisturising cream.

Foster parents should be examined to ensure that they are aware of these issues and are doing something positive about them.

All children needing substitute care, whatever their physical or mental abilities, should have the opportunity to live in a family. The Charter of the National Foster Care Association states that:

The cultural, racial and religious identities of children and young people, their parents and foster carers must be respected in the development of the foster care service and in the making and support of individual placements.

(NFCA, 1987)

Professionals placing black and ethnic minority children who are also mentally handicapped may often have to decide which to prioritise in their search for adoptive and foster parents: the child's racial/ethnic origin or their handicap. Recruitment campaigns should endeavour to attract a wider

IDEAS IN PRACTICE

Waltham Forest Social Services Department employs a senior social worker for people with learning difficulties. They have a same race policy for fostering and adoption of children and have been successful in recruiting Asian foster parents for children with learning difficulties. For adults at present the emphasis is on encouraging same race placement for long term care but giving people the choice about crosscultural respite care and on developing helpful training materials for carers.

Contact: Viroo Bakrania
Senior Social Worker
Pear Tree House
Gorden Road
London E4

Tel: 081 524 1466

pool of black and ethnic minority families in order to avoid this very undesirable situation. The NFCA's charter states that:

The true cost of caring for a foster child or young person must be met, and foster carers given the opportunity to receive payment for their time, energy and skills.

(NFCA, 1987)

However, the allowances provided by some agencies are insufficient to cover the actual costs of giving a child a home. Given the generally poorer economic circumstances of black and ethnic minority families in Britain (Brown, 1984) this issue must be addressed if adequate numbers of black and ethnic minority families are to be found.

Same Race / Transcultural Placing

Over the last ten years the debate on race and the effects of racism has played an increasing role in the development of practice in fostering and adoption. Throughout this process, attitudes have been challenged (Rickford, 1990).

➢ The stereotyped views of the ideal family are gradually changing towards a more flexible approach in finding the appropriate parenting model for individual children.

➢ The myth of the unattainable black foster home is diminishing as black foster and adoptive parents have been successfully recruited.

➢ Those agencies prepared to scrutinise their selection process have proved that black families will come forward when the recruitment methods are more relevant to their background and experiences.

➤ Those authorities which have been most successful in recruiting black people as foster carers have been very active in reaching out to local communities.

In order to ensure that the racial identity of children is considered and their needs are met, some voluntary organisations have committed themselves to the principle of same race placement. Others have gone further in adopting this as policy.

Government guidelines to Social Services directors issued in January 1990 called for "sustained efforts" to recruit sufficient numbers and range of foster parents to meet the needs of children from black and ethnic minority groups or religions. When the Children Act comes into force in October 1991, the guidance will have the force of law. Most authorities seem to be making some effort to address this issue, but the resources they are putting into funding foster placements are very variable (Rickford, 1990).

Take Up of Benefits

The benefits situation for people with learning difficulties is complex. It is generally difficult to find out about what is available and to understand the rules of entitlement. For black and ethnic minority families, this may be further complicated by language differences. As a rule, information is not translated into minority languages and people often do not know which agencies to turn to for advice.

Work by Islington People's Rights has identified comparatively low rates of benefit take up amongst the local Bengali community, including child benefit which is generally widely claimed. Use of day centres by the borough's non-English speaking Greek-Cypriots was also found to be low. A take up campaign amongst this group resulted in receipt by 21 claimants of an annual total of £16,490 in benefits and a further £1,232 in lump sums and arrears (Keeble, 1984). An Asian benefit project in Nottingham similarly raised £6,800 among 75 families and showed that the black community had disproportionately low take up of benefits (Cotmore et al, 1988). Gohil (1987) found a similar situation in Leicester.

The Social Worker knew we had trouble coping because we told her. She has known our family for many years. We still did not find out about our rights to claim attendance allowance, mobility allowance and invalid care allowance. It was another parent we met who told us about all these things. I can't understand why.

Asian Father

The Foleshill study in Coventry highlighted that many Asian families had found out about their entitlement to benefits only by chance.

For example, Ms Sandhu had met another parent at the hospital who had told her about the benefit. She then claimed it successfully, but could have claimed it nine years earlier.

(Cocking and Athwal, 1990)

finding out about benefits can be a full time job —

IDEAS IN PRACTICE

The *Citizens Advice Bureau* in Bradford sees people with learning difficulties and their carers as a priority. Their approach has been to:

➤ identify benefits not taken up

➤ help in the making of claims

➤ follow through every case, visiting families in their homes — some up to seven months later — and challenge refusals where appropriate to the point where benefit is successfully received

They have found this level of support is necessary because carers themselves often do not have the time, energy or knowledge, as one of their case studies illustrates.

We saw Mrs Patel at one of the SECs. Mrs Patel is a widow and has four children, two sons and two daughters. One daughter is mentally handicapped, the other daughter works, one of the two sons works and the younger is still in full time education. Mrs Patel was just getting Widow's Pension. Her daughter who is mentally handicapped was getting SDA and a high Attendance Allowance, they never claimed Supplementary Benefit for her, she is 24 years old

and should have been getting Supplementary Benefit when she left special school. We worked out she was underpaid £18.05 at 1987 rates and was due considerable arrears.

We wrote to the DHSS on behalf of the client asking for an A1 form to claim Supplementary Benefit, the family received the form but the older son refused to claim it on behalf of his sister. We tried to persuade them that there was nothing illegal about claiming what she was entitled to but they were not convinced.

A while back we saw Mrs Patel's daughter who was pleased to inform us that the DHSS had sent them a cheque for her sister amounting to £2000 and that she will be getting Supplementary Benefit from now on.

(BRADFORD CITIZENS ADVICE BUREAU, 1987)

Contact: Janice Fyffe
Bradford Citizens Advice Bureau
12A Ivegate
Bradford BD1 1SW

Tel: 0274 370963

IDEAS IN PRACTICE

Southall Contact a Family have translated all their leaflets on benefits into various languages. These leaflets are available at £1 each.	Contact:	Hardeesh Rai Southall Contact a Family 8–12 Lancaster Road Southall Middlesex UB1 1NW Tel: 081 571 6381

REFERENCES

Akinsola H A A and Fryers T (1986): "A comparison of patterns of disability in severely mentally handicapped children of different ethnic origins". *Psychological Medicine,* Vol 16, pp 127–133.

Baker M R, Banderanayake R and Schweiger M S (1984): "Difference in rate of uptake of immunisation among ethnic groups". *British Medical Journal,* Vol 288, pp 1075–1078.

Balarajan R and Botting B (1989): "Perinatal mortality in England and Wales: Variations by mother's country of birth". *Health Trends,* Vol 21, pp 79–84.

BASW (British Association of Social Workers) Special Interest Group on Services for People with a Mental Handicap (1987): *Newsletter,* No 7, January. Available from John Smith, Treasurer, BASW, 46 Chilton Way, Hungerford, Berkshire RG17 OJF.

BCSG — Black and In Care Steering Group (1984): *Black and In Care. Report of a Conference.* London.

Borum B (1987): "Asian Handicaps". *New Society,* 20 March, pp 22–3.

Bradford Citizens Advice Bureau (CAB) (1987): *Mental Handicap Project.* Bradford, Bradford CAB.

Brown C (1984): *Black and White Britain. The Third PSI Survey.* London, Gower Publishing.

Clarke M and Clayton D G (1983): "Quality of obstetric care provided for Asian immigrants in Leicestershire". *British Medical Journal,* Vol 286, pp 621–623.

Cocking I and Athwal S (1990): "A special case for special treatment". *Social Work Today,* 8 February, pp 12–13.

Contact a Family (1989a): *Reaching Black Families? A Study of Contact a Family in Lewisham and the Relevance of Services for Black Families who have Children with Disabilities and Special Needs.* London, Contact a Family.

Cotmore R et al (1988): *Case Studies in Service Development in Nottinghamshire. A Welfare Rights Initiative.* Loughborough, Loughborough University of Technology, Centre for Research in Social Policy.

Gohil V (1987): "DHSS service delivery to ethnic minority claimants". *Leicester Rights Bulletin,* No 32, June/July, pp 7–8.

Hannam C (1980): *Parents and Mentally Handicapped Children.* Harmondsworth, Penguin.

Keeble (1984): *Disability and Ethnic Minority Groups. A Fact Sheet of Issues and Initiatives.* London, RADAR.

Kumar D, Associate Specialist, Centre for Human Genetics, Sheffield Health Authority (1990): Personal communication, April.

Larbie J (1984): *Black Women and Maternity Services. A Survey of 30 Young Afro-Caribbean Women's Experiences and Perceptions of Pregnancy and Childbirth.* London, Training in Health and Race.

Larbie J, Mares P and Baxter C (1987): *Training Handbook for Multiracial Health Care.* Cambridge, National Extension College.

Lumb K M, Congden P J and Lealman G T (1981): "A comparative review of Asian and British born maternity patients in Bradford 1974–1978". *Journal of Epidemiology and Community Health,* Vol 35, pp 106–109.

Miller E, Nicoll A, Rousseau S A et al (1987): "Congenital rubella in babies of South Asian women in England and Wales: An excess and its causes". *British Medical Journal,* Vol 294, 21 March, pp 737–739.

National Foster Care Association (NFCA) (1987): *Foster Charter.* London, NFCA.

Open University (1986): *Mental Handicap: Patterns for Living.* Course P555. Milton Keynes, Open University.

Open University (1990): *Mental Handicap: Changing Perspectives.* Audio Cassette 2, Side 2, "Making a Case for Change". Milton Keynes, Open University.

Pearson M (ed) (1982): *Issues in Service Delivery to Ethnic Minority Families with Handicapped Children. The Proceedings of a Small Workshop.* Bradford, Centre for Ethnic Minorities Health Studies. Unpublished.

Pearson M (1985): *Racial Equality and Good Practice — Maternity Care.* Cambridge, Health Education Council/National Extension College.

Pearson M (1990): "Ethnic differences in infant health", *Archives of Disease in Childhood*. Forthcoming.

Rao P S S and Inbaraj S G (1980): "Inbreeding effects on foetal growth and development". *Journal of Medical Genetics,* Vol 17, pp 27–31.

Rickford F (1990): "Out of the background". *Social Work Today,* 22 February, p 8.

Rosenthal M, Addison G M and Price D A (1988): "Congenital hypothyroidism: Increased incidence in Asian families". *Archives of Disease in Childhood,* Vol 63, pp 790–93.

Terry P B, Bissenden J G, Condie R G and Mathew P M (1985): "Ethnic differences in congenital malformations". *Archives of Disease in Childhood,* Vol 60, pp 866–8.

Townsend P, Phillimore P and Beattie A (1988): *Health and Deprivation. Inequality and the North.* Beckenham, Croom Helm.

Warburton W (1990a): *Developing Services for Disabled People. Results of an Inspection to Monitor the Operation of the Disabled Persons (Services, Consultation and Representation) Act, 1986.* London, Department of Health, Social Services Inspectorate.

Warburton W (1990b): "Time to turn good intent into action". *Social Work Today,* 22 February, pp 16–17.

Whitfield S, Principal Educational Psychologist, Rochdale Portage Service (1988): Personal communication, December.

Wing L (1969): "Prevalence of different patterns of impairments in immigrants". In Wing J K (ed): *Recent Research in Social Psychiatry.* London, MRC Social Psychiatry Unit, Institute of Psychiatry. Unpublished report.

FURTHER READING

Ahmed A and Pearson M (1985): *Multiracial Initiatives in Maternity Care: Directory of Projects for Black and Ethnic Minority Women.* London, Maternity Alliance.

Brieland D (1969): "Black identity and helping the person". *Children Journal,* September, Vol 16, No 5, pp 150–151.

Bryan B, Dadzie F and Scafe S (1985): *The Heart of the Race: Black Women's Lives in Britain.* London, Virago Press.

Chambers H (1986): "Why black children need black foster parents". *Voluntary Voice,* November, p 10.

Community Care (1989): "A long way still to go". Inside Supplement, 23 February.

Duncan D (ed) (1989): *Working with Bilingual Language Disability.* London, Chapman and Hall.

Edwards J H (1979): "The cost of mutation". In Berg K (ed): *Genetic Damage in Man Caused by Environmental Agents.* New York, Academic Press.

Jervis M (1989): "Cashing in on the hopes of black children". *Social Work Today,* 2 March, pp 14–15.

Jervis M (1990): "Balancing the damage". *Social Work Today,* 8 February, pp 16–17.

Kadushin A (1972): *The Social Work Interview.* Columbia Press.

Leavy W (1987): "Should whites adopt black children?". *Ebony,* September, pp 78–82.

Marett V (1972): "Cross-cultural counselling". *New Community,* Vol 17, No 3.

Oldfield S (1983): *The Counselling Relationship.* London, Routledge and Kegan Paul.

Ranger C (1989): "Language, race and the Children's Bill". *Social Work Today,* 9 March, p 30.

Robinson M J et al (1982): "Ethnic differences in perinatal mortality — A challenge". *Journal of Epidemiology and Community Health,* Vol 36, pp 22–26.

Shackman J (1985): *The Right to be Understood — A Handbook on Working with, Employing and Training Community Interpreters.* Cambridge, National Extension College.

Stewart M (1986): "When black is best". *The Voice,* w/e 1 November, pp 16–17.

Resources

Do you think you are pregnant? — Poster. *Are you pregnant?* — Leaflets in various Asian languages. All are available from the Health Education Authority, Hamilton House, Mabledon Place, London WC1H 9TX.

Be prepared, be happy — 16mm film or video. Antenatal care from a young Asian woman's perspective. Available in various Asian languages. From CFL Vision, Sales Department, Chalfont Grove, Gerrards Cross, Bucks SL9 8TN.

Having your baby in Britain — Cassette tape, 24 mins, 71 colour slides. Produced by Medway Health District and the Community Relations Council, it covers antenatal to postnatal care. Available from Graves Medical Audio Visual Ltd, Holly House, 220 New London Road, Chelmsford, Essex CM2 9BJ.

Communication Techniques — VHS/Betamax video and training manual. The video illustrates language and communication difficulties at home, in the clinic and in hospital and gives examples of good practice. Available from the Royal Society of Medicine Services Ltd, Film and Television Unit, Royal Society of Medicine, 1 Wimpole Street, London W1M 8AE.

Role of the Linkworker — VHS/Betamax video. Training video which highlights the difficulties of health professionals at service delivery points in overcoming communication difficulties and assessing the needs of pregnant women. Available from the Royal Society of Medicine Services (see above for address).

Cross Talk is the second film in the series "Multiracial Britain". The focus is on crosscultural communication between those in authority and black and ethnic minority people. Available for hire from Concord Films, 201 Felixstowe Road, Ipswich IP3 9BJ. Tel: 0473 715754. Available to buy from the HEA, Hamilton House, Mabledon Place, London WC1H 9TX. An accompanying booklet costs £1.

Communication Techniques is a training video in three parts in English for use in linkworker training. Produced for the Asian Mother and Baby Campaign by the Save the Children Fund. Available from NHS Training Authority, Media Development Unit, Eastwood Park, Falfield, Wotton-under-Edge, Glos GL12 8AD.

The Role of the Linkworker is a video in English, also produced for the Asian Mother and Baby Campaign, and available from the NHSTA (see above for details).

Physical and Mental Handicap in the Asian Community — Can My Child be Helped? — A VHS video (with supporting booklet) is available in five languages of the Indian Sub-Continent (Urdu, Punjabi, Gujarati, Hindi, Bengali) and in English. It is for use by Asian families with a young disabled child. It was produced by the Voluntary Council for Handicapped Children with support from the Department of Health. Purchase £29.50, hire £10.50. Available from CFL Vision, PO Box 35, Wetherby, West Yorkshire LS23 7GX. For further information, contact Philippa Russell, Voluntary Council for Handicapped Children, 8 Wakley Street, London EC1V 7QE. Tel: 071 278 9441.

Awaaz: Help for Parents of Children with Special Needs — A 53 minute video and 24 page booklet produced by Manchester Council for Community Relations, with support from the King's Fund Carers Unit. Available December 1990 in Asian languages and English. It aims to give parents of children with special needs information and advice about benefits, services and support, including:

➢ your child's disability

➢ financial help

➢ social services and social workers

➢ education

➢ disabled young people of 16 and over

➢ the future

Contact: Robina Shah, Awaaz
Manchester Council for Community Relations
3 Jacksons Row
Deansgate
Manchester M2 5WD
Tel: 061 834 9153

The Right to be Understood — A video about working with interpreters. Available from the National Extension College, 18 Brooklands Avenue, Cambridge CB2 2HN. Tel: 0223 316644.

Be My Parent — British Agencies for Adoption and Fostering's Family Finding book and video services to enable prospective parents to get to know as much as possible about, and get a feeling for, the children concerned. Contact British Agencies for Adoption and Fostering (address below).

Black and In Care — In this video children talk about their experiences of being in care and how they have and are trying to overcome their difficulties. Available from Black and In Care Steering Group, c/o Children's Legal Centre, 20 Compton Terrace, London N1 2UN. Tel: 071 359 6251. Cost £32.50 plus 50p postage.

The Good Feeling of Fostering features African, Afro-Caribbean, Asian and White foster families in homely settings — reflecting the different cultures. It is for use by social workers for recruitment purposes. Available from Fosterfacts (address below).

The Children's Society has launched a recruitment video for black adoptive parents. It is for use with individual enquirers and with groups, and will also be available to other adoption and fostering agencies. For more information, contact Steve Jenkins. Tel: 071 837 4299 ext 244.

ORGANISATIONS

African Family Advisory Service
Goldhawk House
49 Goldhawk Road
London W12 8QP
Tel: 01 749 7324

Jointly funded by the DoH, the London Boroughs Grant Scheme and the Save the Children Fund. Advises local authorities on issues affecting West African families and children in the UK.

British Agencies for Adoption and Fostering
11 Southwark Street
London SE1
Tel: 071 407 8800

Children First in Transracial Fostering and Adoption
37 Warner Road
London N8 7HB
Tel: 081 341 7190

Fosterfacts
c/o Mr Philip Barron
3rd Floor, 3 Henrietta Street
Covent Garden
London WC2 8LU
Tel: 071 240 2656

An information service for people enquiring about fostering in the Greater London area and a resource centre for people professionally involved. Produces information, leaflets and other materials for child foster campaign directed at members of the Afro-Caribbean and Asian communities.

National Foster Care Association
25–27 Elmbank Street
Glasgow G2 4PB
Tel: 041 226 3431

National Foster Care Association
Francis House
Francis Street
London SW1P 1DE

Tel: 071 828 6266

Parent to Parent
Lower Boddington
Daventry
Northamptonshire NN11 6YB

Tel: 0327 60295

Provides information on adoption services and will direct you to local branches nationally.

Pre-School

Before this, there was nothing for us. I felt completely isolated from our own people and from everybody else. It was terrible. I did not know what I could do to help my child. Coming here has helped me to talk. We have also together found out how to help our children. Parveen now has friends at the group. She is a lot happier which makes me happy as well.

Mother, Asian Opportunity Group

Introduction

The pre-school years can be a difficult time for many parents who have a child or children with learning difficulties. For some the learning difficulty will not have been identified until well after birth; for all it will be a time of change and adjustment. Often parents may be left with inadequate support and help. For black and ethnic minority parents, the situation may be particularly bleak. Their access to services is likely to be poor, perhaps because of language differences or because services are inappropriate. As with the white community the mother is usually the main carer. Powell and Perkins (1984) in their study found that Asian mothers were "assuming almost total responsibility for the day to day care of their handicapped child".

This chapter explores services that are essential to give families help, guidance, support and information in the pre- school years.

➢ Support for Parents
➢ Play, Opportunity Groups and Toy Libraries
➢ Portage
➢ Speech Therapy
➢ Physiotherapy

As in Chapter 2, many of the issues addressed here will also apply to other age groups.

SUPPORT FOR PARENTS

The stigma of having a handicapped child produces a reserve in others, it is not meant to be unfriendly, it is embarrassment, a sense of inadequacy and possibly a fear of contamination which holds others back.

(HANNAM, 1980)

Society generally does not value people with learning difficulties. At best they are pitied and treated with charity; at worst they are shunned. For parents who love their children and see them as individuals, society's reactions can be very painful. One Asian father said that other people's comments "cut through his heart like a knife". Another Asian mother commented that some people thought that their children would become like her own daughter if they were allowed to mix. Negative attitudes and ignorance, coupled with inappropriate services, reinforce social and physical isolation.

Most of the research carried out amongst black women carers points to their extreme isolation. The myth of the cohesion of Asian communities belies the loneliness and isolation faced by many carers. Black and ethnic minority people may have a greater need for support than their white peers. Migration may have severed their traditional networks of support. Even where there are relatives in Britain, they may live in other cities. Many black and ethnic minority carers to whom we spoke felt isolated and desperate.

I would just sit and stare at those four walls, I thought I was the only one with all these problems. I would cry a lot, especially when my husband was not here ... I felt like running away, I felt I couldn't cope. It was all too much and no-one to talk to ... I cannot even begin to explain how difficult it has been for me to pass these years, I wouldn't know where to begin.

ASIAN MOTHER

I used to spend mostly all my time indoors with him seven days a week without anybody to help except when I take him to see my mother and even that was a great problem to wait by the bus stop. He used to run in the road sometimes because he don't really want me to hold his hand all the time. He used to touch and push people with a smile on his face and people think he was being very rude.

People used to give him funny looks and push him aside and call him naughty boy. He would just be smiling and trying to be friendly. Nobody did understand he has problems, not unless I told them.

I manage to cope until he was four and three months and it came the stage that I could not cope anymore. Then the social worker suggested I need a break once a month from Friday to Monday.

(JULES, 1987)

Our contacts with voluntary organisations working with young children with learning difficulties indicated that very few realised the extent to which their services were inappropriate and inaccessible to black and ethnic minority people. Comments such as "we don't make any distinction between different people", and "we treat all people the same" were common.

It is all too easy to assume black and ethnic minority families' needs without finding out. Consultation is of paramount importance. It should involve in-depth liaison work between professionals and the black and ethnic minority communities concerned. (Further suggestions about consultation are outlined in Chapter 8.)

Support Groups

In recognition of the many difficulties which parents face during the pre-school years, various support groups and linking agencies have been established.

Attending a support group can provide a forum where parents can overcome problems faced on many different levels. An immediate effect can be to relieve some of the extreme isolation and loneliness. The mutual support which parents in similar circumstances can give each other can be an enhancing experience.

A support group can provide:

➢ emotional support and the opportunity for some to actually talk at length, for the first time, about their child's difficulties

➢ the opportunity to identify mutual problems and to do something about them. For example, English tuition; bringing in health professionals to explain more clearly what different disabilities are and the various services available

➢ an arena to develop as a pressure group in order to campaign for better services

Outreach work will be vital to the development of support groups to include black and ethnic minority people. Visiting families at home will be important in publicising the group and in establishing people's needs and priorities.

As the group develops, outreach work will be important in following through problems identified during meetings. It also provides an opportunity to visit carers who may be unable to attend the group but nevertheless need support and help.

Voluntary and statutory agencies interested in providing support for *all* parents in their area can learn a lot from existing black parent groups.

The Association for the Support of Asian Parents with Handicapped Children

This is a voluntary group which was started by Muslim parents in Walthamstow with the help of the head teacher of Grosvenor House School, Sylvia Sullivan. Many parents felt that their needs and concerns were not being heard or addressed by the schools their children were attending. In setting up this group, parents have been able to become far more active in their children's education, as well as being able to support each other. Apart from providing emotional support, they have also been able to mobilise resources in order to lobby for better services. One result has been the setting up of a Saturday group for their children, which can provide activities which are additional to school life. (See Chapter 3, page 96.) However, they would like to see schools taking up such issues and activities themselves.

Nazar Hussain, the co-ordinator of the group, feels strongly that Asian parents must be enabled to participate fully in assessment procedures and must have a voice in decisions made about their children's lives. In this respect, the group tries to ensure that all parents are informed about important meetings and relevant conferences. They try to ensure that informal advocates are available for parents who either speak little English or are intimidated by the system. This has been particularly important in getting more parents involved in assessment procedures.

The group has also been able to build up strong links with other organisations such as the local Community Health Council, and to put issues on the agenda which would otherwise not be addressed.

Contact: Nazar Hussain
           Association for the Support of Asian
                Parents with Handicapped
                Children
           378 Hoe Street
           Grosvenor House School
           Walthamstow
           London E17
           Tel: 081 556 5123

For an illustrated account of the group, see Kelly (1987).

IDEAS IN PRACTICE

Contact A Family

Contact a Family is a national charity which assists families who have children aged from birth to 19 with different types of disabilities and special needs.

The aim of local projects is to put families who have children with different disabilities and special needs in touch with one another so that they can offer support, advice and encouragement to each other. From this initial contact, mutual support and self-help groups are developed.

Lewisham Contact a Family have developed an initiative for reaching black and ethnic minority families of children with special needs, including the establishment of Asian and Afro-Caribbean parent support groups. (For details, see Chapter 8, page 191.)

Southall Contact a Family has one full time and one half time worker. The project in Southall caters for children who have a wide range of disabilities and special needs. The project primarily aims to meet the needs of Asian families, although there are other families who are part of the group who do not come from the Asian community. The predominant languages within the scheme are Punjabi, Hindi, Urdu and Gujarati. All information is provided in these languages.

The project tries to meet a wide variety of needs, ranging from giving parents advice on welfare rights, to holiday provision for children and parents. Playschemes are an important part of the work but other aspects include parent meetings, a Saturday Club, newsletters and social and fundraising events. Volunteers have a vital role in the work. Also important is the organisation of transport rotas for families who would otherwise be unable to get to many of the activities that are arranged (Rai, 1989).

The Southall Under Fives Group

The Southall Under Fives Group are planning to form a support network for families with a special needs child who is under the age of five. They have employed an Asian play leader, who teaches the children games, songs and movement. Families whose first language is not English are especially welcome and encouraged to attend and it is hoped to provide information and support in Asian languages. The group hopes to meet informally to share ideas and experiences and organise activities.

Specific Aims

➤ to make contact through health clinics and special day nurseries with families of young children with special needs

➤ to organise activities with creche facilities for parents of under-fives

➤ to help parents to understand their welfare rights and information on benefits

➤ to gain a better understanding of Special Education and prepare families for procedures preceding school

➤ to form support groups for children's assessment procedures (see section on assessment in Chapter 4, page 86)

All these aims will be fulfilled by working closely with an existing Contact a Family group and staff.

At present there are six children under the age of five waiting to join the group with their mothers, who have no access to any other support group.

Contact: Hardeesh Rai
           Southall Contact a Family
           8–12 Lancaster Road
           Southall
           Middlesex UB1 1NW
           Tel: 081 571 6381

Sandwell Asian Family Support Service (SAFSS): Invalid Children's Aid Nationwide (ICAN) Asian Family Support Centre

SAFSS started out with funds from ICAN and provides a personalised service offering families practical help and continuing moral and emotional support as required. This can range from making a cup of tea to guidance on using the welfare benefit system.

Each family is visited at least once a week. Help and support is offered to parents in their contact with special schools and hospitals (for example, helping parents to accept their child's learning difficulties). They have appointed a care assistant who will go into families to help them (for example, preparing children to be ready for school, or helping feed a child who takes up a lot of the mother's time).

Contact: Sheila Mall, Co-ordinator
Sandwell Asian Family Support
 Service
176 Windmill Lane
Smethwick, Warley
West Midlands B66 3NA

Tel: 021 558 2198

Play, Opportunity Groups, Toys and Toy Libraries

Opportunities for play and mixing with other children are vitally important for all pre-school children, including those with learning difficulties. They provide children with stimulation and the scope for development. Play facility organisers must consider how to meet the needs of black and ethnic minority children in their area.

Play

The emphasis placed on different modes of learning (for example, passive versus active involvement, the use of touch, imagination and symbolism in play) is socially and culturally determined. This will be reflected in the types and modes of play which children are encouraged to develop, in decisions about what to play with, or when to change from one play activity to another, and how success is measured in accomplishing a task.

In our communities children and adults are not kept apart from each other to the extent that they are in the white community. There is less distinction between those social activities which are considered exclusively for children or for adults. Children attend and participate in events in the community such as celebrations, weddings, christenings, funerals and demonstrations, rallies or whatever. Adults have as much fun at a child's birthday party as the children themselves. Through this mixing, children gradually learn skills and social roles. There is less dependence on bought toys or formal instruction and teaching for this to happen.

Afro-Caribbean Mother

A recent report (Commission for Racial Equality, 1989) points out that children begin to form ideas about race and racial prejudice from a very early age. By the age of three, children have already formed distinct impressions about the value of being white or black in our society. Attitudes towards skin colour and the value we attach to it are easily picked up, not only through other people's responses, but also from the media.

If differences between children are not valued then black and ethnic minority children are likely to grow up with a low self- esteem, thinking that there is something wrong with them and their cultural background. As Rayside (1987) points out, all too often children are unwittingly expected to play the "white way". She cites the example of an Asian girl, who was making tea just like her mum by boiling the tea, milk and sugar all together in a saucepan. She was told by the playworker:

No dear, don't use the saucepan, here is the teapot.

ANTIRACIST CHILDCARE

➢ Workers should actively intervene where black and ethnic minority children may be victimised because of their colour or other aspects of their behaviour which are linked to their cultural background (for example, the way they speak).

➢ If children are curious about colour differences and ask questions, the issues should be explored positively and answers given, albeit in simple terms.

For example:

"Why is Angela black?" can be answered simply, "Her mother and/or father are/is black". This is what very young children want to know. Older children may be asking about what makes skin black and they can be told about melanin. Sidestepping by saying, "All people are alike" or "Colour doesn't matter" denies the differences which the children can see and are asking about and could convey a message to them that being different is something to be ashamed of.

(Brown, 1988)

Opportunity Groups

Opportunity groups are playgroups which deliberately cater for a mixture of children with and without handicaps, thus providing important models and early experiences for both. Opportunity groups may well also provide a base for other services for the child and its family, for parent groups and workshops, for example, or a toy library.

Toys

Toys are a key feature of playgroups, nurseries and opportunity groups and have an important role to play in children's development generally. There is an increasing awareness of the importance of providing appropriate toys and playing environments for a multicultural, multiracial society.

➢ **Toys for education** — Using toys for educational purposes may be new to some parents who may consider toys as purely recreational. It is important to discuss the role of toys as educational tools so that all parents can understand their positive role in a child's development.

➢ **Buying toys** — On the whole, Asian parents are less likely to consider buying toys for their children a priority (Ghuman, 1975). For some, this will be a result of limited financial resources, for others, using "everyday items" for play will be just as important as buying toys. It is important to build upon this view. Parents can be encouraged to view everyday items as useful educational tools (for example, putting

Khass

Khass is an opportunity group for Asian mothers with a handicapped child in Bristol. It was set up in February 1988 with support from the Bristol Inner City Health Project. The group has a two-fold function. It provides play facilities for children with learning difficulties and their able-bodied siblings, as well as giving parents an opportunity to meet, share experiences and offer support to each other.

Parents can feel confident that their children are receiving good care, thus allowing them to concentrate on some of their own needs. The group has provided an ideal opportunity for parents to identify their common problems and establish ways of overcoming them.

A need for English language tuition was felt to be particularly important. A tutor now regularly attends the meetings Because parents also felt that they did not have enough contact with their children's special schools a visit was arranged. For many of the mothers this was an emotional experience. Seeing their children in the school context, and perhaps doing things they had not realised them capable of, was revealing and positive.

On the whole the company and support provided by other parents in similar circumstances was highly valued.

Contact:

Rushda Munir
Parent Support Worker
Khass Asian Opportunity Group
St Werburghs Community Centre
Horley Road
Bristol BS2 9TJ

The Khass Evaluation Report is now available from:

The Public Relations Department
Bristol and Weston Health Authority
Manulife House
Marlborough Street
Bristol BS1 3NP

Tel: 0272 290666

IDEAS IN PRACTICE

Toy Libraries

Tower Hamlets Portage Centre — The toy library has recently acquired black dolls and other toys reflecting their surrounding communities. About 10–15 Bengali parents regularly bring their children with learning difficulties and their siblings to the toy library. This creates a healthy atmosphere of mixing children of different learning abilities as well as solving the problem of childminding for other children.

Bengali parents who attend the toy library have also begun to form a Parents' Group, allowing them to focus on their difficulties and begin to establish a self-help group.

The Toy Library is run by a Bengali woman. Originally, there was resistance by some workers to having her in this post, as she cannot speak English, and it was felt that she would not be able to cope. However, it has proved a great success; she has personally developed a greater sense of self-confidence and other parents can relate to her.

(See page 74 for further details about the Tower Hamlets Portage Centre.)

Blue Gate Toy Library — Playgroup and toy library organisers who wish to improve services would benefit from the following approach used with Bengali families at the Bluegate Toy Library in Tower Hamlets. Its success was demonstrated by the increase in the number of such families using the group. From their experience, organisers of playgroups and toy libraries should ensure that:

➤ black and ethnic minority parents are aware that these facilities exist

  Past experience of inappropriate services will make many black and ethnic minority parents suspicious of what is available. It is important to demonstrate that these groups have changed, or are willing to change, in order to meet their needs.

➤ publicity is translated into relevant languages and displayed in public places black and ethnic minority people are likely to frequent

  For example, local health centres, places of worship (like gurdwaras, mosques and local black churches).

➤ bilingual staff are employed in order to personally visit families and tell them about available services

➤ positive attempts are made to involve black and ethnic minority parents and use this opportunity to gain a closer understanding of their needs and priorities

➤ the environment and activities are reflective of all the different backgrounds of the children attending

  For example, posters, pictures, books and other materials should be multiracial/ multicultural, depicting all ethnic groups in a positive way. Music, games, nursery rhymes and toys from Asian, Afro-Caribbean and other communities should be included.

➤ volunteers are recruited from black and ethnic minority communities

The Bluegate Toy Library gets funds from a variety of sources, including the Toy Library Association.

Contact: Nancy Seddington
    Blue Gate Fields Junior School
    King David Lane
    London E1
    Tel: 071 790 3613

knives, forks and spoons into appropriate compartments can develop the same sorting skills as expensive, bought toys).

➤ **Appropriate toys** — The visual imagery we present to children is very important. Many images stereotype minority groups. If all cultures are to be valued and celebrated, then positive images should be fostered by toy libraries through the toys and books offered.

PORTAGE

Portage is a home visiting scheme in which parents of children with learning difficulties are trained by a home teacher how to teach their children particular skills and tasks. The scheme is based on the idea that parents are keen to maximise their child's development, and that given training, they can easily learn to do this. The home teacher (who may be a teacher, a nursery nurse, a health visitor or someone without a professional qualification but with training in portage) first assesses the child. On the basis of this assessment the mother and teacher together will choose, and practise, suitable tasks for the mother (or other relative) to teach the child during the forthcoming week. The results are recorded on an activity chart (Ward, 1982).

This model of working with parents is based on a system established in the United States in the late 1960s and was introduced to Britain in 1976. The National Portage Association estimates that there are currently about 100 home teaching and 50 school based portage schemes in existence in the UK.

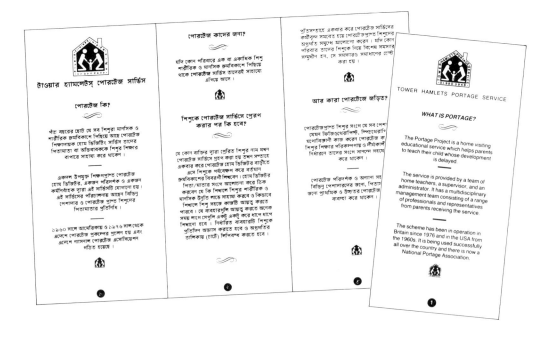

Its principles and house style have wider applications. Work done in this country and elsewhere, for example, in Zimbabwe (Russell, 1988), clearly shows that partnership with parents is productive and warmly welcomed when the context is appropriate to the needs of the child and family.

Several authors (Bardsley and Perkins, 1983; Powell and Perkins, 1984; Smith and Sayeed, 1986) have looked at the conceptual and practical considerations which must be addressed when providing portage to Asian communities. They include the awareness of culturally appropriate developmental norms, appreciation of different ways of rearing children, the need for effective forms of communication and appreciation of different roles within the family.

Powell and Perkins (1984) demonstrated that portage can be of benefit to people with learning difficulties from black and ethnic minority families in Britain. However, it has not on the whole been widely pursued in these communities. The following are two areas of particular concern.

➤ **Lack of knowledge** — Sufficient attention has not been paid to ensure that black and ethnic minority families understand and appreciate the aims and methods of the portage system. The experience of portage workers shows that many families do not have a general understanding of their child's learning difficulties. Greater attention has to be paid to explaining portage to them.

➤ **Conflict of views** — People from different cultural backgrounds will obviously have different priorities for what they believe their children should be taught. For some families, teaching may be synonymous with learning only cognitive skills. Their ideas and priorities may differ from the wider brief of social and self-help skills which underlie the portage system.

Portage workers must be wary of assuming that black and ethnic minority families will share the same ideas and values as themselves. On the whole, home advisers have to approach black and ethnic minority families with an open mind and be prepared to be flexible. Misunderstandings can often develop if this is not the case.

It is vital that home advisers and others in the portage team take time to establish the families' own priorities. For example, ideas about childrearing may be different.

➤ Should children be educated consciously from a very early age or should they pick up things as they grow older?

➤ Is a routine essential for their security and discipline or should they be cared for, bathed and so forth, whenever they need it and it is convenient?

A Way Forward

Our discussions with families and portage workers have suggested the following ways forward.

➤ **Pre-portage training** — Given the gaps in services to black and ethnic minority families, there is need for pre-portage training for both families and professionals. This would aim to discuss the underlying concepts of portage, particularly the parents' own roles as teachers and the important part they can play in their child's learning processes. Parents and professionals would share ideas and come closer to an understanding of each other. Training for staff, as suggested by the Tower Hamlets Portage Centre, should include:

— awareness of personal attitudes and stereotypes towards different racial and cultural groups

— ways of working with black and ethnic minority families with a sensitive and flexible approach

— recognition of pre-existing skills and different cultural expectations

➤ **Working with the family as a whole** — Contact with families may identify other areas of need, not directly connected with portage (such as entitlement to benefits, housing conditions), which will, in their turn, influence the family's ability to spend time with their child. It is important to deal with these issues, if not personally, at least by bringing in relevant professionals.

You have to see the family as a whole and not just the little child on its own. For example, if the mother has no washing machine then she will be hand washing all day and not doing portage. These things are important and people don't realise it.

Mrs Sayeed, Tower Hamlets Portage Centre

➤ **A flexible approach** — Successful work with families will require flexibility on the part of portage workers to ensure that the timing and content of portage tasks are suitable for the individual families. If both parents are working, the only time they will have available for portage tasks will be during the evening. The Tower Hamlets scheme has taken steps to visit parents in the evening. Workers also need to be sensitive to different family structures and the roles members play. For example, it may be important to include grandmothers in portage as they may take a leading role in care.

The following accounts from Tower Hamlets Portage Centre demonstrate the need for flexibility in portage.

A Bengali mother who was a recent migrant had very little concept of the western time and day systems. She had to be taught how to use the calendar and clock. This was important not only for preparing the mother for portage, but also for helping her to acquire skills relevant to living in Britain. In this particular case it was very important that the mother was taught a western concept of time as her child was also epileptic and so it was important to administer drugs at the appropriate time. This had not been identified and tackled by health professionals.

(SMITH AND SAYEED, 1986)

Desmond, a three year old boy whose parents are from Jamaica, had a general developmental delay, was fostered by his elderly grandparents who were very keen to co-operate with the home visitors. However, it soon became clear that two standards of performance were in operation. For example, in a home-based feeding programme designed to increase his self-feeding skills with solids, it was found out that Desmond's grandmother was giving him several feeding bottles at meal times because she had to rush out to a job and did not have time to allow him to "mess about with food". When Desmond's grandfather, who was at home all day, was asked if he could help with feeding, it became apparent that he had never considered it to be something he should be doing. After much anxiety about this lack of success, it was decided that the grandfather should be invited to the unit in order to show staff how he helped his grandson at home. This was a great success, after which Desmond not only ate well in the unit, but his grandfather also made sure that he ate at home too.

(SMITH AND SAYEED, 1986)

➤ **Adaptation of material** — An important challenge to portage will be to translate materials into the language used by the family, where this is appropriate. If parents are not literate in their own language, other alternatives have to be found. For example, the Tower Hamlets Portage Centre are considering tape recording instructions in relevant languages.

Care has to be taken where any material is translated, as the adaptation from one language to another is an intricate process. It is not simply a word for word translation, but also a culturally relevant adaptation. If translations are inadequate, they can often convey the wrong meaning. For example, one Bengali mother whom we interviewed had received a letter from her child's school recommending that her daughter see a psychologist. However, the translation implied that her child might be "mad". This caused her great anxiety and confusion.

Tower Hamlets Portage Centre

In working with Bengali families, Asian home advisers at Tower Hamlets Portage Centre take the following approach:

➤ an initial visit to introduce herself and let the family get to know her

At this point conversation is general and discussion may be around the family's life situation and other difficulties they may be facing. Much depends on this initial contact, as the building of a trusting relationship between home adviser and carers is essential.

➤ a second visit to fill in appropriate forms and continue with confidence building

➤ a third visit where portage is spoken about in depth for the first time

The home adviser tries to explain the concepts and procedures followed in simple, unjargoned language, giving carers enough time to understand and ask questions.

Portage schemes should consider how to incorporate these points into the structure of their overall framework of portage delivery.

Contact: Fawzia Peermamode
Tower Hamlets Portage Centre
Mowlem Street
Bishopsway
London E2 9HE
Tel: 081 980 3948

➤ **Interpreters** — It is becoming increasingly clear that direct verbal communication has the most positive outcome in working with families. If a bilingual portage worker is not available, it is vital that an interpreter is involved and trained appropriately (see Chapter 2 for a fuller discussion).

➤ **Counselling** — Since many parents may not understand fully their child's difficulties, never having had a proper explanation, home advisers may find that parents have not fully realised and accepted their child's "handicap".

Portage workers in Tower Hamlets found that mothers who had not yet gone through the important process of "grieving" about their loss, were unable to begin to come to terms with the situation. In such circumstances, parents' emotional needs must be addressed, either by the portage worker, or someone else appropriate, before portage can be started successfully. An Asian co-ordinator of a portage scheme in

Tower Hamlets believes that counselling will inevitably become part of the portage worker's role, but many find this controversial since it crosses the boundaries of workers' perceived roles. There may be resistance by portage workers who may not see counselling as their responsibility.

➤ **Employment of black and ethnic minority portage workers** — Employment of home advisers from the local communities is vital to improve services. They will speak the same language and be generally sensitive to local families' circumstances. Although the important role of para-professionals in portage is recognised, there has been little effort to recruit as portage workers black and ethnic minority people with the relevant knowledge and cultural sensitivity. (For further details on black staff, see Chapter 7.)

SPEECH THERAPY

People with learning difficulties, by definition, will need longer to learn to express themselves. It is difficult, if not impossible, for a speech therapist who is not familiar with the language and culture of their client to identify problems such as slow development of speech, and to determine the extent of the difficulty and the help required. Problems will inevitably arise unless a co-ordinated attempt is made to enable black and ethnic minority people with learning difficulties to speak and communicate in their mother tongue (see box overleaf, *Mrs Ahmed's Story*).

➤ **The importance of using the mother tongue** — Black and ethnic people with learning difficulties may be required to use one language in speech therapy and another at home. The two environments frequently exist as separate entities with little communication or continuity between them. This is likely to delay the development of speech. Where speech therapy is given in English without consideration to the child's home language, it may lead to difficulties of communication between children and parents. If the mother tongue is discouraged, black and ethnic minority people with language difficulties may begin to feel that the language spoken at home is inferior.

➤ **Communication is more than language** — It is not sufficient, and can be dangerous, for English speaking speech therapists to know a list of Asian words which are used in assessing the stage of speech development. Language is inextricably bound up with culture and is expressed through body language and other non-verbal forms of communication. Hand and facial gestures as well as the sounds a child makes in learning to speak are all influenced by cultural background.

MRS AHMED'S STORY

Mrs Ahmed, a young mother, has three daughters under the age of five. Mrs Ahmed speaks Urdu and some basic English. Her eldest daughter aged four was identified by a speech therapist as having slow language development. After this she attended speech therapy sessions. Since these sessions were carried out in English, Mrs Ahmed's daughter now mainly speaks English. This has meant that mother and daughter now have difficulty communicating, often leading to frustration and tension.

➤ **Assessing English as a second language** — Different uses of the English language need to be taken into consideration. For example, the sentence structure and word emphasis may be different for people who speak English as a second language. Many Afro-Caribbeans speak a form of patois which, although it is derived largely from English, has developed its own structure and meaning.

➤ **Merged language development** — Where children move regularly between different cultural and language situations, language development will merge. For example, English words may be incorporated into Punjabi sentences (Madhani, 1989). This will inevitably make language assessment more difficult.

Improving Speech Therapy for Black and Ethnic Minority Clients

On the basis of our review of the literature on bilingualism (see especially Duncan, 1989), and discussions with people with learning difficulties and their families and with speech therapists we recommend that:

➤ more effort should be made to employ and train bilingual speech therapists

➤ for staff who only speak English, it is important to gain a sound knowledge of the social, economic and historical context of the people with whom they work

➤ speech therapists must work closely with parents and families in order to gain a better understanding of the child's abilities

➤ interagency liaison is important to ensure that the initiatives of bilingual speech therapy are maintained throughout all services being used by the child

➤ training for speech therapists must encompass issues surrounding bi/multilingualism

➤ it is important that the wider issues around assessment of bilingual children with learning difficulties are considered

(These issues are discussed further in Chapter 4.)

The College of Speech Therapists have a fuller paper on these issues. *Guidelines for Good Practice for Speech Therapists Working with Clients from Linguistic Minority Communities* (1990) is available from:

> The College of Speech Therapists
> Harold Porter House
> 6 Lechmere Road
> London NW2
> Tel: 081 459 8521

Or: Mr Sam Abudarham
> School of Speech Therapy
> Birmingham Polytechnic
> Perrybar
> Birmingham B42 2SU
> Tel: 021 331 5485

PHYSIOTHERAPY

Physiotherapy may be an important part of the care programme for some children and adults with learning difficulties, particularly those who also have physical disabilities. To be successful, physiotherapy needs to be carried out in partnership with people with learning difficulties and their families. Depending on their familiarity with and acceptance of western medicine, families will have different ideas about physical propriety.

It is important to find out the attitudes, knowledge and preferences of families and ensure that they are given adequate explanation about the benefits of physiotherapy. The scope and limitations of this form of therapy should be adequately explained to avoid unrealistic optimism and the resulting frustration and confusion that often occurs.

It may be necessary to have therapists of the same sex if this is required. Where activities such as dancing and swimming are felt to be needed, there may be a need for single sex sessions and appropriate modest swimwear for women. Care needs to be taken in ensuring that the families' wishes regarding modesty and appropriate behaviour are respected. This will have implications for activities such as massaging and limb manipulation.

REFERENCES

Bardsley J and Perkins E (1983): *Portage with Asian Families in Central Birmingham. Parents as Partners.* Proceedings of the National Portage Conference held in London, NFER-Nelson.

Brown B (1988): "Anti-racist practice is good practice". *Nursing World,* 22 September.

Child E (1985): "Play and Culture. A study of English and Asian children". *Leisure Studies,* No 2, pp 169–186.

Commission for Racial Equality (CRE) (1989): *From Cradle to School — A Practical Guide.* London, Commission for Racial Equality.

Contact a Family (1989a): *Reaching Black Families? A Study of Contact a Family in Lewisham and the Relevance of Services for Black Families who have Children with Disabilities and Special Needs.* London, Contact a Family.

Duncan D (1989): *Working with Bilingual Language Disability.* London, Chapman and Hall.

Ghuman P (1975): *The Cultural Context of Thinking.* Windsor, NFER-Nelson.

Hannam C (1980): *Parents and Mentally Handicapped Children.* Harmondsworth, Penguin.

Jules M (1987): *Wesley, My Only Son.* London, Centreprise.

Kelly C (1987): "Finding a voice". *Community Care,* 31 December, pp 22–25.

Madhani N (1989): "First language Punjabi development". In Duncan D (ed): *Working with Bilingual Language Disability.* London, Chapman and Hall.

Powell M and Perkins E (1984): "Asian families with a pre-school handicapped child — A study". *Mental Handicap,* Vol 12, pp 50–52.

Rai H (1989): "Introductory speech". In *The Educational Needs of Ethnic Minority Children who have Disabilities and Special Needs.* London, Contact a Family.

Rayside V (1987): "My Identity". *Nursery World,* 29 January.

Russell P (1988): "Partnership with parents". *Community Care,* 14 July, pp 29–31.

Smith S and Sayeed A (1986): *Portage and Ethnic Minority Groups.* Unpublished paper presented to National Portage Conference, Winchester.

Ward L (1982): *People First. Developing Services in the Community for People with Mental Handicap.* London, King's Fund Centre.

Further Reading

Commission for Racial Equality (CRE) (1977): *Caring for Under-Fives in a Multi-Racial Society*. London, Commission for Racial Equality.

Council on Inter-Racial Books for Children: *Bulletin*. 1841, Broadway, New York, NY 10023.

Council on Interracial Books for Children (1983): *Childcare Shapes the Future: Anti-Racist Strategies*. Audio-visual programme and presenter's guide. New York, Council on Interracial Books for Children.

Cunningham C and Davis H (1985): *Working with Parents: Frameworks for Collaboration*. Milton Keynes, Open University Press.

Daley et al (ed) (1985): *Portage: The Importance of Parents*. Windsor, NFER-Nelson.

GLC Women's Committee (1986): *Childcare Our Way — A Report by the GLC Women's Committee with the Black and Ethnic Minority Childcare Group*. London, Women's Equality Group, Room 401, Middlesex House, 20 Vauxhall Bridge Road.

ILEA Equal Opportunities Unit (1986): *Nursery Rhyme or Reason — A Report of the Working Party on the Care of the Under Fives*. London, ILEA.

Interdepartmental Consultative Group on the Provision of Services for Under Fives from Ethnic Minority Communities (1984): *Services for Under Fives from Ethnic Minority Communities*. London, Department of Health and Social Security.

Moodley K (1985): "Education and the underfives: An opportunity to be equal? The end or the beginning? Achievement and underachievement — A dual responsibility". *Multicultural Teaching*, Spring, Vol 111, No 2.

Resources

Toys and Books for Children

Criteria for the Assessment of Literature and Learning Resources for Young People: An Anti-Racist Perspective. From Librarians Anti-Racist Strategies Group (for address, see Organisations).

New Beacon Books — General Catalogue, including Children's Books — of Black British, Caribbean, African, Afro-American, Afro-European and other general materials. For parents, students, teachers and others. From New Beacon Books, 76 Stroud Green Road, London N4 3EN. Tel: 071 272 4889.

Five Ways to Analyse Children's Books for Racism — Leaflet. Building Blocks, Cultural Action Under Fives, Resources and Training Centre, Castlemead Estate, The Rampway, Camberwell Road, London SE5.

Resources for an Anti-Racist Strategy for the Under-Fives

Celestin N (1986): *A Guide to Anti-Racist Childcare Practice.* London, Voluntary Organisations Liaison Council for Under Fives.

ILEA Anti-Racist Strategies and Practices in Early Year and Primary Education Working Party (1986): *Racist, Non-Racist and Anti-Racist Resources in Early Childhood.* ILEA Centre for Anti-Racist Education, Mawbey School, Cooper's Road, London SE1 5DA.

ILEA Equal Opportunities Employment Unit (1986): *Working Together — Good Practice Guidelines for GLC/ILEA Day Nurseries.* ILEA.

Resources for Anti-Racist Education. Information leaflet. Afro-Caribbean Education Resource Centre, Wyvil School, Wyvil Road, London SW8 2TJ.

Video

Let's Play Colour. Antiracist Childcare. Available from East Birmingham Health Education Department, 102 Blaksley Road, Yardley, Birmingham B25 8RN.

Organisations

Access to Information on Multicultural Education Resources (AIMER)
Faculty of Education and Community Studies
University of Reading
Bulmershe Court
Earley
Reading RG6 1HY
Tel: 0734 663387

Afro-Caribbean Education Resources Project (ACER)
Wyvil School
Wyvil Road
London SW8 2TJ
Tel: 071 627 2662

Librarians Anti-Racist Strategies Group
(A group of WGARCR, see below.)
c/o Shusil Sharma
Ethnic Minorities Librarian
LB Hounslow
Neville Close
Lampton Road
Hounslow
Middlesex

National Children's Bureau — The Under Fives Unit
NCB, Under Fives Unit
8 Wakley Street
London EC1V 7QE
Tel: 071 278 9441

Will provide references to literature relevant to equality of opportunity and antiracist childcare/education organisation and practice.

Nursery Nurse Trainers Anti-Racist Network
1 The Lyndens
51 Granville Road
London N12 0JH

Pre-school Playgroups Association
61–63 King's Cross Road
London WC1X 9LL
Tel: 071 833 0991

Voluntary Organisations Liaison Council for Under Fives (VOLCUF)
77 Holloway Road
London N7 8JZ
Tel: 071 607 9573

Working Group Against Racism in Children's Resources (WGARCR)
460 Wandsworth Road
London SW8
Tel: 071 627 4594

THE SCHOOL AGE CHILD

Parents, you must mobilise yourselves, you must get together so that you can put your case. You must implement your rights. You have rights as parents. You have a right to have your child accurately statemented. You have a right to speech therapy, you have a right to home helps, you have a right to aids and adaptations for your home. Your rights do not just extend to school. They extend beyond that. You must get together and achieve these rights.

Dr Abrol, Head Teacher of Mayfield Special School
(Contact a Family, 1989b)

INTRODUCTION

In this chapter we will be looking at the concerns of black and ethnic minority parents with a school age child with learning difficulties.

➢ Assessment Procedures
➢ Education
➢ Home–School Liaison
➢ Respite Care
➢ Transition to Adulthood

Residential care, in which some school age children may be placed, is discussed in Chapter 5.

ASSESSMENT PROCEDURES

When I look at some of the Asian children, I can tell by their eyes that they don't have a mental handicap. If only they could speak English we would know better.

MEMBER OF TEACHING STAFF

In Chapter 1 we looked at some of the main causes for concern about the assessment of black and ethnic minority children with learning difficulties. Over the last twenty years, there has been a growing body of opinion that inappropriate assessment procedures might be amongst the factors contributing to the disproportionate numbers of black and ethnic minority children assessed as having *moderate* learning difficulties and placed in special schools (Coard, 1971; Tomlinson, 1982).

Recently similar anxieties have been expressed about the over-representation of ethnic minority children in schools for those with *severe* learning difficulties. In 1986, it was reported that over 40% of the Bangladeshi children with special needs in Tower Hamlets were in these schools, yet the overall figure in inner London was only 17.0%. Many Bangladeshi parents were worried that their children had been assessed in English, saying that they would have been able to carry out the required tasks if the assessment had been in their own language (Chaudhury, 1986).

There is a major concern that children for whom English is a second language are being disproportionately placed in schools and units for children with (severe) learning difficulties. A report by Her Majesty's

Inspectorate in 1983 on a school in Bradford for pupils with learning difficulties noted that 23% of these children spoke English as a second language, often with delayed speech and language (Tomlinson, 1989). An ILEA report, on the other hand, found that no particular ethnic minority group was over-represented in special schools overall (ILEA, 1984).

Involving Parents in Assessment

Statementing is a statutory requirement for identifying the educational support required by children with special needs, including those with learning difficulties. The important role of parents in this process has been recognised by the 1981 Education Act. This set out to provide a framework within which parents would have rights of involvement throughout assessment procedures resulting in the "statementing" of their children.

However, it is still difficult for many parents to understand the complex and highly bureaucratic assessment and review procedures, or to make full use of their rights. For parents from black and ethnic minority communities, involvement is made even more difficult.

➤ Formal letters proposing assessment or annual reviews may not be translated for, or understood by parents (Rehal, 1989).

➤ The onus is often on the parent who does not speak English to find an interpreter. This will usually be a family member or a friend — not necessarily well versed in educational terminology or procedure. This is an increasing area of concern to families (Contact a Family, 1989a).

➤ Parents may believe that "special" education means that it is of "better quality" than general schools (Chaudhury, 1988).

If the 1981 Education Act is to be taken seriously, then services have to enable all parents to participate. The Advisory Centre for Education (1989) recommends that Authorities should:

➤ ensure "that a competent bilingual professional" is involved in the proceedings throughout

➤ translate all materials used

➤ arrange meetings where parents who have children with learning difficulties can meet and discuss common concerns

Adopting these recommendations would go some way towards addressing the failure of the education system to involve black and ethnic minority parents who have children with learning difficulties.

Parental Involvement in Assessment and Special Educational Provision

The Department of Education and Science has funded the Voluntary Council for Handicapped Children to carry out a project looking at parental involvement in assessment and special educational provision. A major part of this work will be to explore ways of involving and supporting parents from black and ethnic minority communities, and to develop information and training material with these communities for their use.

Contact: Philippa Russell or Sheila Gatiss
               Voluntary Council for Handicapped Children
               8 Wakley Street
               London EC1V 7QE

               Tel: 071 278 9441

Assessing the Educational Needs of Ethnic Minority Children who have Disabilities and Special Needs

In April 1989, Southall Contact a Family organised a conference to address the issues faced by black and ethnic minority families of children with special needs. Dr Surdashan Abrol, the Head Teacher of Mayfield Special School in Birmingham, gave a keynote speech based on both her professional experience of teaching in India and in England, and her personal experience as a mother of a daughter with cerebral palsy. Dr Abrol challenged parents to make their opinions known within the schools so that a partnership of parents and teachers could be developed. Many useful and important issues were raised, including parents' attitudes towards the educational system in the UK, and the need to adapt language systems such as Makaton to take account of the needs of children whose first language is not English.

A number of ideas for improving the current situation emerged at the conference, including the following.

➢ Parents should be seen as partners in the education of their children.

➢ Statementing reports should be produced in the parents' first language, in addition to English.

➢ Professionals are often not aware, or sensitive to, the needs of bilingual pupils. More bilingual staff are needed within schools.

➢ People with disabilities need to be consulted on educational issues.

➢ Tests and assessment procedures are not free of cultural bias. It is important for this to be kept in mind and to be eliminated as far as possible when reviews are taking place.

➢ Tapes should be produced in different languages which explain the statementing procedure to parents.

The Conference report (Contact a Family, 1989b) includes Dr Abrol's keynote address plus a full account of the discussions and recommendations relevant to all educational authorities. It will be a useful resource for parents, teachers and anyone else interested in special education, and is available from:

Contact a Family
16 Strutton Ground
Victoria
London SW1P 2HP
Tel: 071 222 2695

IDEAS IN PRACTICE

Centre for Multicultural Education in Cleveland

This Centre employs a member of staff to assist with bilingual assessment of children, including those with special needs. The focus of the teacher's work is as follows:

➤ to appraise and support special needs pupils, whether in special schools' units or mainstream

➤ to work closely with medical and education services and the county psychological service in formal assessment of pupils

➤ to advise and support parents in the placement of their child and to encourage parents to become involved in the child's education

➤ to follow initial assessment, depending on the level of need, and offer advice, guidance and support to the school and teachers as appropriate

➤ to develop materials and teaching techniques

➤ to organise and hold classes for parents and the community in sign language, to assist hearing impaired children

The work of the teacher is carried out in close liaison with schools. The post is funded through Section 11 funding (see Chapter 7, page 178).

Contact: Mrs Anu Hansarni
Centre for Multicultural Education
Victoria Road School
Victoria Road
Middlesborough
Cleveland TS1 3QF
Tel: 0642 219050

Advisory Centre for Education (ACE) Bangladeshi Parent Advice Service

The ACE "Special Education" Advice Service was set up to advise and support Bangladeshi parents in Tower Hamlets whose children were being assessed for, or were already receiving, "special education". The work was funded by the Commission for Racial Equality.

To ensure that parents were fully informed ACE recommended that they be given a flow chart (in English and Bengali) which showed the stages at which they, as parents, would be able to contribute to the assessment. The chart also contained information on whom parents could contact for further information in the authority; and the names and addresses and telephone numbers of organisations which could give independent advice.

This is also a good idea for agencies working within other bilingual communities. Although this project no longer exists, getting in touch with ACE about how they developed their flow charts would provide an important starting point for similar initiatives.

A report of a conference, *Asian Children with Special Needs*, organised by ACE, Commission for Racial Equality, Tower Hamlets Council for Racial Equality and Inner London Education Authority in November 1989 is also available from ACE and costs £3.

Contact: ACE (Education Advice Service)
18 Victoria Park Square
London E2 9PB
Tel: 081 980 4596

Education

The debate over whether children with learning difficulties should attend special schools or be part of mainstream services is slowly moving in favour of greater integration. Nevertheless the majority of children with learning difficulties will spend their school-age years in special schools.

For black and ethnic minority communities there are two major concerns about educational services offered to children. They are:

➢ the misplacement of black and ethnic minority children in special schools or other segregated services such as special units

➢ inappropriate services owing to a lack of appreciation of individuals' different cultural and social needs

Abrol (1990) and Tomlinson (1989) outline some of the main concerns about the appropriateness of established education content and methods for black and ethnic minority children.

Curriculum Content

In several curriculum areas, minority cultures are either misunderstood or are undervalued in a curriculum which reflects the majority culture. This may alienate parents and children. For example, where the purpose of teaching "life skills" is to enable students to become more independent it is important that the skills taught are relevant to the pupils' daily lives.

➢ Most Asian people prefer to take a shower rather than a bath, even if this means using a bucket of warm water and a jug where no shower unit is available. Using a bath is considered unhygienic, with dirt from all over the body mingling with the fixed volume of water in the bath.

➢ Eating with the fingers is actively discouraged in most schools. Two distinctive eating methods are, therefore, imposed on Asian pupils: on the one hand they are taught to eat chapati and dal with their hands at home, and on the other hand they must use a knife and fork at school.

➢ Minority greetings such as "Sat-Shri-Akal", "Namaste" and "Salam-la-kam" are rarely taught. When an adult speaks to a child in the Asian community, the child is told not to look the adult in the face. In the host community the opposite practice is encouraged. Many uninformed white teachers may interpret the Asian child's behaviour as rude or insolent rather than as a sign of respect.

Language

Teaching pupils in English may add to their learning difficulties. In addition to the issues discussed in the section on Speech Therapy (Chapter 2, page 75), exposure all day to an unfamiliar language, together with the school culture, may bewilder pupils. English speaking teachers may misinterpret children's speech. For example, an Asian child may begin to babble the word "abba" (dad) at home, encouraged by his/her parents. In the school, ignorant of Asian languages, a monolingual, English speaking teacher may try to develop the child's babbling sound as "ba ba" or "bye bye" (Abrol, 1990).

Racist Stereotypes

Racist stereotypes and biased presentations persist in many of the books and teaching materials used in schools. An analysis of their content reveals that many are based on white Anglo-Saxon Protestant values which are patronising and dismissive of other cultures, religions and societies (CRE, 1981).

Overt Racism at School

There is a misguided belief that black and ethnic minority children with learning difficulties do not perceive racism as other children do, and, therefore, it is not as important to be vigilant over what is taught in special schools. In Foleshill, an Asian boy with learning difficulties felt unable to share with his mother his distress about racist taunts at school (Coventry Social Services, 1986). At a recent conference in London for black people with learning difficulties, many participants had experienced overt racism, both from other white people with learning difficulties and from white staff (Baxter, 1990a). One woman, for example, said:

People think that black people and Indian people come to this country and cause violence. They blame them.

Others said they felt different because of their colour and were called names such as "black bastard".

A Way Forward

It is essential that the CRE's recommendation (CRE, 1981) that

educational aims for the curriculum should include the preparation of young people for life in a multiracial society and the promotion of good race relations

is taken on board by Education Authorities in curriculum development for special school education.

➢ It is vital that all training for teachers is strongly grounded in an antiracist approach. Teachers are the most important people in

IDEAS IN PRACTICE

Coventry Minority Group Service

Coventry Education Authority has a Minority Group Support Service (MGSS) for teachers in special schools. Their role is to provide direct help for ethnic minority pupils and assist special schools in developing English as a second language. The special school staff are an integral part of the MGSS team. The work of these special school teachers is essentially innovative. Their professional duties and responsibilities include:

➤ a consultative/advisory role to provide information and resources for multicultural education in special schools

➤ initiating and assisting in the development of supportive learning programmes in multicultural curriculum initiatives

➤ assisting as required in the provision of in-service training on an ongoing basis, pertinent to the needs of children from ethnic minority backgrounds

➤ working with specialist welfare staff to provide home–school liaison — providing assistance in the transition of pupils between mainstream and special schools

➤ contributing to reviews, reports and mandatory assessments

➤ providing effective liaison between the schools and home and/or other agencies

➤ providing resources and programmes for English as a second language learning experience as the need arises

➤ undertaking special projects as requested by the head of service or on their own initiative

Contact: Chris Shearsby
Acting Head of Service
Minority Group Support Service
Coventry Education Authority
South Street
Hillsfields
Coventry
Tel: 0203 226888

---

implementing antiracist policies and must, themselves, be aware of the issues. This can only be achieved by ensuring that "initial and in-service training is permeated consciously by a multiracial perspective" (CRE, 1981). (For more information on staff development and training, see Chapter 8.)

➤ It is also vital to ensure that black and ethnic minority teachers are proportionately represented in all schools. Employing black and ethnic minority teachers is important in ensuring not only that black and ethnic minority children with learning difficulties have positive role models in positions of relative power, but also that *all* children in the school relate to black teachers in important positions, and see it as a natural part of belonging to a multiracial society. (See also Chapter 7, on recruitment of black and ethnic minority staff.)

Home–School Liaison

To ensure the best possible progress for a child with learning difficulties, school and parents must work closely together, each aware of what is happening to the child in these two separate domains. However, it has been well documented that contact is often minimal between black and ethnic minority parents (particularly those for whom English is not their first language) and the schools their children attend (Jervis, 1987). Several factors are involved.

For parents whose first language is not English, the problems faced in trying to communicate with English speaking teachers may be compounded by the use by professionals of jargon, and vague or contradictory medical and psychological terminology (Tomlinson, 1989). In a survey of Asian parents of handicapped children in Smethwick, three quarters of the mothers and half of the fathers spoke no English, but their children received their schooling in English (Woolley and Dhanoa, 1985). Communication problems between the school, the home and the child with learning difficulties were thus exacerbated.

Given these language issues, it is not surprising that many parents do not participate in school activities such as parents' meetings. This is often taken by the school to mean that parents are not interested in their children's education or are seen to be hostile to the school and all it stands for. In fact, black and ethnic minority parents often feel alienated from the school environment which reflects a strong white middle class ethos reinforced by the lack of black staff.

One father who spoke fluent English and was very interested in his child's education wanted to approach us to see what progress his child was making. However, as he explained, he was so intimidated he had to get his brothers to take time off work to accompany him.

SCHOOL HEAD TEACHER

➤ **Information and communication** — Appropriate means of disseminating information has to be a high priority. All leaflets and letters referring to parents' rights and obligations, their child's assessment, school activities and parents meetings should be translated into relevant languages.

➤ **Black and/or bilingual home–school liaison teachers** — These are of paramount importance, providing an invaluable resource to schools and crucial in building links with parents. However, few authorities are prepared to provide such a service, which may be seen as an optional "luxury". Moreover, where such posts are established, they may be particularly vulnerable to cuts in the education budget. In Bradford in 1988, 80 such posts were not filled, owing to financial cuts (Tomlinson, 1989).

IDEAS IN PRACTICE

Home–School Liaison Worker for the Asian Community

Wilson Stuart School in Birmingham appointed a Home–School Liaison Worker for the Asian community. She related:

We try to gain their [Asian parents] confidence by putting labels and signs in their home language. Changing displays to reflect their cultural and historical background encourages them to come.

FROM "WOMEN HOLD UP HALF THE SKY", LINK PROGRAMME, CENTRAL TELEVISION

Contact: Mr Colin Grantham, Head Teacher
Wilson Stuart School
Perny Common Road
Erdington
Birmingham B23 7AT
Tel: 021 373 4475

The following special schools also employ Home–School Liaison Officers:

Beatrice Tate School
St Jude's Road
London E2
Tel: 071 739 6249

Branshaw School
(Contact: Gillian Hughes)
Oxford Street
Oakworth Road
Keighley
West Yorkshire BD21 1QX
Tel: 0535 662739

> **Parent governors** — With the advent of Local Management of Schools (Education Act, 1988) school governors will have increasing responsibility in the way schools are run, who is employed and how budgets are spent. Head teachers and governors alike need to review how black and ethnic minority parents can be enabled to participate more in the life of the special schools their children attend — and encouraged to become school governors themselves.

Advocacy

The role of black and ethnic minority communities in providing advocacy is well established (see Chapter 5, page 141, for further discussion of advocacy schemes).

Some black voluntary organisations act as informal advocates for parents in the school environment. **Southall Contact a Family** (see pages 64 and 89) try to:

> act as "friends" to families as distinct from professionals

> avoid using technical language

> establish links with professionals

> support and inform parents in the assessment process

The Association for the Support of Asian Parents with Handicapped Children (see Chapter 3, page 63) also try to provide informal advocacy for parents within the educational system.

Saturday Group at Waltham Forest

In 1985, the Association for the Support of Asian Parents with Handicapped Children set up a Saturday Group at Grosvenor House School for physically and mentally handicapped children. They are funded by an Urban Aid Grant as well as some local Asian businesses.

Every Saturday a paid volunteer picks up the children in a mini-bus. Sometimes their (young) brothers and sisters come along as well.

Activities during the gathering are firmly centred around the home culture of these children. Hindi music provides a backdrop to many of the activities. Posters and books give positive images of black and ethnic minority people. Other activities, such as Asian cooking and games, give the children skills which are relevant to their own cultural background.

Mr Hussain, Co-ordinator of the Association, actively tries to recruit Asian volunteers to work with the group. He feels that the children need to relate to people from their own background as well as others to help them to build up positive self-images. (See Chapter 3, page 63, for further information on this group.)

Contact: Mr Nazir Hussain
Association for the Support of
Asian Parents with
Handicapped Children
378 Hoe Street
Grosvenor School
Walthamstow
London E17

Tel: 081 556 5123

RESPITE CARE

Family based respite care — where children with handicaps spend short periods in the home of another family — is increasingly recognised as an important part of service provision. Short-term respite can, if provided sensitively, enhance the lives of children with learning difficulties, by giving them the opportunity for new experiences and relationships, and also help their families, by giving them a break.

The National Association for Family Based Respite Care estimates that there are now approximately 280 such schemes around Britain. Schemes vary enormously. Their common feature is the linking of a family with a handicapped child — via an independent agency (most commonly a local authority social services department or a voluntary body like Barnado's) — to another individual or family who is paid expenses to provide regular or occasional respite care.

In respite care schemes throughout Britain, black and ethnic minority families are less likely to be involved than their white peers.

➢ In a study in Avon, both Asian and Afro-Caribbean families were under-represented among respite care users yet figured prominently amongst the group of non-users who said they had not received adequate information about the service (Robinson, 1988).

➢ In reply to our questionnaire, Leeds Social Services Department stated that although they administer one of the biggest family placement schemes in the UK (with 168 children involved plus 90 children receiving short term care in two residential homes), they cater for only about 10 children from black and ethnic minority communities.

It is often assumed that black and ethnic minority families prefer to "look after their own". However, experience has shown that black and ethnic minority families can and do want to use respite services. Schemes like Bradford's "Give Mum a Break" and Barnado's "Families Together" in Tower Hamlets have demonstrated that lack of initiative on behalf of service providers may explain the low take up. Their experience suggests that there are three major issues which schemes must tackle:

➢ information and communication difficulties
➢ parents' concerns about how black children will be looked after
➢ the availability of black carers and professionals to service schemes

Information and Communication

Problems of access to information and of language and communication difficulties have been discussed in previous sections. These issues can have a profound impact on individuals.

An Asian widow, herself disabled, with several children including a son with severe learning difficulties, had been without support or benefits for the four years since her husband died. Soon after her bereavement she had been visited by a social worker and offered respite care for her son. Unable to fully understand the conversation and believing the intention was to take the child away on a permanent basis, the mother refused the offer. She was left to cope on her own until Contact a Family became involved four years later.

CO-ORDINATOR, SOUTHALL CONTACT A FAMILY

Services like Give Mum a Break in Bradford, Barnardo's Families Together in Tower Hamlets, and Contact a Family in Lewisham and Southall (Contact a Family, 1989a, b) have tackled communication issues in a number of ways. Their experience suggests the following approaches.

➢ Black and ethnic minority workers who speak appropriate community languages should be employed on schemes. They should preferably be women, since much of the work is inevitably with mothers. The experience of Give Mum a Break confirms that interpreters are a much inferior alternative to the direct employment of black service workers who can both communicate adequately with clients *and* deal with substantive issues that arise (rather than just translating).

➢ Publicity and other material must be produced in relevant community languages, with photos/illustrations reflecting the neighbourhood to be served. Christine Lenahan, Project Worker with Barnardo's in Tower Hamlets, points out that translating their information for the local Bangladeshi community was not straightforward. Many of the English words used had no Bengali equivalent, but virtually all their written information is now available in Bengali and their ansaphone message is in Sylheti. In Bradford, Give Mum a Break leaflets are now produced in four Asian languages. Other written materials (like application and assessment forms) have also been translated.

➢ Traditional (white English) means of publicity should be reviewed. In Bradford, the Asian worker employed at Give Mum a Break was able to identify more appropriate ways of publicising their service. She used her personal contacts and identified clinics and shops — textiles, greengrocers, etc. — which were used by Asian people, which were ideal for the exchange and passing on of information. Additional avenues for disseminating information include talking on local Asian radio programmes and putting articles and advertisements in Asian magazines.

➢ The best publicity for a service and its usefulness is its obvious success in helping a family. Too often services seem to be waiting for a big demand before taking any action. It may be important to start small — with just a few families — providing an appropriate, acceptable and useful service which will build up the confidence of the community as a whole. The need for such confidence building should not be underestimated. There is an overwhelming feeling amongst black and ethnic minority communities that services are not geared to meeting their needs — that they must adapt to fit in with established service systems, rather than vice versa.

How Will the Children be Looked After ?

In one study in Avon, 73% of parents expressed guilt or apprehension about their handicapped child staying away from home for the first time (Robinson, 1988). For black and ethnic minority parents, such anxieties are aggravated by additional concerns. In Britain black and ethnic minority people's ways of life are often viewed as inferior and families may have had direct experience of such attitudes. In the absence of black and ethnic minority families to provide respite care, parents are naturally uneasy about their handicapped child going into a strange family environment where their needs may be viewed as a problem.

➢ Worries about the likelihood of inappropriate and unfamiliar diet, lack of attention to cultural practices, should be dealt with by thorough preparation and adequate introductions for both families (and children) involved in the respite care process. Information about hair and skin care, toileting or personal care routines, dietary preferences should automatically be exchanged in this way — as they should be for a white child staying with another English family for the first time. (See also the section on personal care in Chapter 5, page 124.)

Religious observance may be a particular concern. Religion for many Asian people is not just about attending the gurdwara, mosque or temple. It is a way of life. People who are not strictly religious may lead a life based on the principles of their religious background.

Mr and Mrs Rafiq are unhappy when they make use of their local scheme, that their son Nadeen is unable to pray during Ramadan as they would like. His religious and cultural practices are not respected and his diet suffers. Mr and Mrs Hussain worry about their daughter Parveen being looked after in someone else's home now that she is physically mature. They fear the possibility of sexual exploitation.

For Afro-Caribbean families there are parallel concerns about inappropriate, and damaging, hair and skin care and worries about the possibility of racism and its effects on their child.

(POONIA AND WARD, 1990)

Recent research suggests that black families are more likely to be users of institution based respite services than family based ones (Nottingham SSD, 1987; Robinson and Stalker, 1989).

➤ Staff and management will need to be encouraged to adopt a more flexible approach to customary routines and practices. They will need to make a conscious effort to find out from black families what they require.

Recruiting Black and Ethnic Minority Respite Carers

A survey by Nottingham Social Services Department (1987) identified reluctance among black families to use short term care services. They expressed a clear preference for "same race" placements for their relative when talking about future accommodation needs. Same race placements are increasingly the accepted norm in mainstream fostering and adoption services (see Chapter 2, page 47). Experience in Nottingham and elsewhere demonstrates that black care families do exist.

The recruitment of such families as carers may be increased by the employment of black and ethnic minority staff to service respite schemes. Black and ethnic minority professionals and carers are not hard to find when a positive effort is made (see Chapter 7). For example, when an Asian worker was initially employed by Give Mum a Break in Bradford, only three Asian families had expressed interest in using the scheme, and only two had offered to become carers. By November 1988, 120 Asian children were using the service offered by 60 care families (Poonia and Ward, 1990).

The recruitment of black "support families" demands flexibility and new ways of working, not only in the distribution of publicity material but in agency procedures. At the moment, these vary widely from one scheme to another.

In one city, for example, Mr and Mrs Rafiq pay their brother Nazar Shah on a private basis to provide occasional respite for their son. The local respite care scheme will not regularise this situation. Mr Shah cannot be formally employed on the scheme (which would enable Mr and Mrs Rafiq to have access to respite care free of charge, as they would if their son went to a white English care family) because Mr Rafiq and Mr Shah are close relatives and there is fear of the system being "abused". In another city nearby, however, the approach is more flexible and close relatives can be involved.

Mr and Mrs Uppal have an acquaintance — Mrs Atwal — who would like to provide respite care for their daughter. The local scheme does not support the arrangement because it would not be "flexible" from the scheme's point of view. "Flexibility" here means flexibility for the agency not the individuals concerned. This particular scheme is somewhat unusual in requiring that every support family becomes involved with more than one family requiring respite care. So Mrs Atwal, who only wishes to look after Rajinder, will not fit the bill.

In Tower Hamlets, the Barnardo's project workers soon realised that the very means of assessment used in assessing the suitability of support families were culturally biased. For example, the principle that people living in "overcrowded accommodation" could not be approved as support carers was based on different definitions of what constitutes overcrowding — and involved the risk of excluding many families from the Indian subcontinent living in the UK. Project staff have had to struggle to find replacement assessment systems which achieve the overriding goal — which is to find out what it would be like to a handicapped child to be looked after by a potential support family.

(Poonia and Ward, 1990)

Schemes should also be prepared, like Give Mum a Break in Bradford, to take verbal as well as written references on the suitability of care families.

Contact: Christine Lenahan
Families Together
76 Wentworth Street
Tower Hamlets
London
Tel: 01 375 2273

Or: Geoff Green
Bradford Family Placement Schemes
2 Springfield
Squire Lane
Bradford BD7 6RA
Tel: 0274 490944

Transition to Adulthood

Adolescence

As "children" grow out of statutory definitions of childhood, many of the support services on which parents rely may be suddenly withdrawn. For example, respite care services may be for "children only". A young person may have to change to a different "adult" service institution to get respite care. School will stop. There may be no places available in Adult Training Centres. This transition may, therefore, be a time of additional stress for parents.

As children with learning difficulties enter adulthood, they, like other young people, will go through a period of transition. Concepts of what an "adolescent period" means vary between cultures. Adolescence in the white majority culture may be associated with carefree rebellion. However, children from black and ethnic minority families may be expected to ease into adulthood by taking on responsibilities from an early age. There may, therefore, be a conflict of expectations of white staff and black and ethnic minority parents as to how young people should behave during this time.

There may also be different views about parent–child relationships as children get older. For many black and ethnic minority people with learning difficulties, the family will remain a central focus. This contrasts with an increasing emphasis in the white community on young adults developing a life independent of the family. This will have implications for preparing children for life after school and the types of options presented to them by service professionals.

Nazir's Story

Nazir is 15 years old. He is one of four children. His mother is widowed. As he has got older, Nazir has assumed responsibility at home. He has become increasingly protective towards his mother and ensures that his younger siblings pull their weight around the house. His mother is very proud of her son and his willingness to take on this role of responsibility and care. Some of this behaviour carries over into the special school he attends, where he sometimes continues to assert his big brother image. The staff at the school interpret his attempts at responsibility very negatively. One member of staff commented:

As he has got older the Asianness in Nazir is beginning to come out. He orders us around because we are women and is aggressive with it. He is always asking if we have done the teas and telling us when it is time for a break.

This view of his behaviour has led to Nazir becoming more isolated at school.

Physical Care

There is also the case of a very small built Muslim woman who is caring for her adolescent, hemiplegic daughter. The frequent lifting and turning to provide those intimate services during bathing and toileting increased the physical demands on the mother. The male members cannot be involved in this aspect of care because of the need to observe the religious duties to maintain modesty at all times. Despite repeated explanations, the family's social worker fails to appreciate the importance of this and, therefore, does not feel it necessary to assist this family in getting help.

(BAXTER, 1989)

In most communities, issues associated with menstruation are treated with great modesty. This aspect of physical care of young women must be handled sensitively. In most families in most communities it will not be acceptable for a male relative to attend to the intimate personal care of girls. This could cause extreme embarrassment to all concerned and may involve breaches of religious codes of conduct which could have deep and meaningful implications. The reluctance of male relatives to become involved in this aspect of care should not be misinterpreted.

➤ It is important to find out from families if there are any customs which they wish to be observed around the time of menstruation.

➤ Families may be anxious that their daughter's or son's contact with adults of the opposite sex during puberty does not conflict with their religious beliefs.

Other issues relevant to the transition to adulthood — like personal relationships, sexuality and marriage — are discussed in Chapter 5.

References

Abrol S (1990): "Curriculum and culture". *Special Children,* February, pp 8–10.

Advisory Centre for Education (ACE) (1989): *Asian Children with Special Needs.* London, Advisory Centre for Education (Education Advice Service).

Baxter C (1989): "A spotlight on unmet need — Black carers in Focus". *Care Link,* Spring, pp 4–5.

Baxter C (1990a): *Sharing Experiences to Challenge Practice. A Report of Two Workshops Around Services for Black People with Learning Difficulties.* London, CCETSW. Forthcoming.

Chaudhury A (1986): *ACE "Special Education" Advice Service for the Bangladeshi Community.* London, Advisory Centre for Education.

Chaudhury A (1988): "How special is special?" *Issues,* Spring.

Coard B (1971): *How the West Indian Child is made Educationally Subnormal in the British School System.* London, New Beacon Books.

Commission for Racial Equality (CRE) (1981): *Local Education Authorities and the Implications of Section 71 of the Race Relations Act 1976.* London, Commission for Racial Equality.

Contact a Family (1989a): *Reaching Black Families? A Study of Contact a Family in Lewisham and the Relevance of Services for Black Families who have Children with Disabilities and Special Needs.* London, Contact a Family.

Contact a Family (1989b): *The Educational Needs of Ethnic Minority Children who have Disabilities and Special Needs.* London, Contact a Family.

Coventry Social Services Department (1986): *The Foleshill Mental Handicap Study.* Coventry, Social Services Research Unit. Unpublished.

ILEA Research and Statistics (1984): *Characteristics of Pupils in Special Schools.* London, ILEA.

Jervis M (1987): "Across the cultural divide". *Special Children,* March, pp 20–22.

Poonia K and Ward L (1990): "A fair share of the care?" *Community Care,* January 11, pp 16–18.

Rehal A (1989): "Involving Asian parents in the statementing procedure. The way forward". *Educational Psychology in Practice,* pp 189–192.

Robinson C (1988): "Home from home?" In Wedge P (ed): *Social Work — A Third Look at Research into Practice.* Birmingham, BASW.

Robinson C and Stalker K (1989): *Time for a Break*. Bristol, University of Bristol, Norah Fry Research Centre.

Tomlinson S (1982): *Educational Subnormality. A Study in Decision Making.* London, Routledge and Keagan Paul.

Tomlinson S (1989): "Asian pupils and special issues". *British Journal of Special Education,* September, Vol 16, No 3, pp 119–122.

Woolley A and Dhanoa B (1985): *A Study of Asian Families with Handicapped Children in Smethwick.* London, ICAA.

FURTHER READING

Davis H and Chaudhury P (1988): "Helping Bangladeshi families: Tower Hamlets Parent Adviser Scheme". *Mental Handicap,* June, pp 48–51.

Greater London Association for Disabled People (GLAD) (1987): *Disability and Ethnic Minority Communities. A study in three London Boroughs.* London, Greater London Association for Disabled People. Available from GLAD, 336 Brixton Road, London SW9 7AA. Tel: 071 274 0107.

Home Affairs Committee (1986–87): *Bangladeshis in Britain,* Vol 1. London, HMSO.

Mittler P (1989): "Warnock and Swann: Similarities and differences". In Verma G K (ed): *Education for All: A Landmark in Pluralism.* London, Macmillian.

Nottingham Social Services Department (1987): *Sample Study of Black Families with a Mentally Handicapped Member.* Nottingham SSD Research Unit. Unpublished.

Wolfendale S et al (ed) (1988): "Educational psychologists working in multi-cultural communities: Training and practice". *The British Psychological Society,* Vol 5, No 2.

The following publications relate to education in a multiracial society generally, and not specifically to people with learning difficulties.

The Burnage Report (1989): *Murder in the Playground. The Report of the MacDonald Enquiry into Racism and Racial Violence in Manchester Schools.* London, Longsight.

Commission for Racial Equality (CRE) (1985): *Towards Genuine Consultation: Principles of Community Participation.* London, CRE.

Commission for Racial Equality (CRE) (1988): *Learning in Terror: A Survey of Racial Harassment in Schools and Colleges.* London, CRE.

The Runnymede Trust (1987): *Teaching for Equality: Educational Resources on Race and Gender.* London, Runnymede Trust.

RESOURCES

A Welcome Break is a video which looks at the Shared Care Scheme operating in Birmingham. Parents of children with disabilities describe the pressures and difficulties of caring for their children, and the help given by the Shared Care Scheme. The ordinary people who are hosts (carers) on the scheme talk about their experiences and the fulfilment they gain.

The video illustrates how respite care can be given in a flexible, friendly manner, with relationships developing between hosts, children and their parents enabling all parties to feel relaxed and at home. The need for black hosts for black children is clearly addressed.

The video is ideal for those professionals who might be wanting to set up such a scheme or students examining the needs of people with disabilities and examples of good practice. It is a very useful recruitment tool in the search for carers and clearly explains the scheme to potential users.

Price £9.99 plus p & p. Available in English (running time 30 minutes) and Punjabi (15 minutes) from Shared Care Team, Birmingham Social Services, Ladywood Area Office, 23 All Saints Road, Hockley, Birmingham.
Tel: 021 523 4361.

ADULTHOOD

As I am now, they feel that I don't know much. I want them to understand that, although I'm disabled, I have a lot of sense and understanding. I can lead a normal life. I can do anything. I can say what I want.

(WILTSHIRE, 1985)

INTRODUCTION

In this chapter we explore some of the key services and important issues which affect the lives of black and ethnic minority adults with learning difficulties.

- ➢ Further and Adult Education
- ➢ Adult Training Centres
- ➢ Employment
- ➢ Residential Services
- ➢ Personal Relationships, Leisure and Recreation
- ➢ Advocacy
- ➢ Challenging Behaviour

Further and Adult Education

For all young people, the transition from school to adult life can be a complex and difficult process. It may be more difficult if the young person has learning difficulties and additionally so if the young person is from a black or an ethnic minority group.

The 1988 Education Reform Act states that it is the duty of every local education authority to provide adequate facilities for further education in their area, including provision for those people over school leaving age who have learning difficulties. In implementing the Act, local authorities are required to produce a broad strategic plan for further education. This is an ideal opportunity for education authorities to develop a holistic approach which embraces multiculturalism and special needs, within the framework of education for all and an antiracist approach.

The challenges in further education parallel those facing schools. Issues regarding curriculum and policy development as well as staff training and recruitment have to embrace the needs and concerns of a multiracial, multicultural society. Thus, many of the issues and strategies outlined in the section on education in Chapter 4 also apply to this chapter.

Ideas In Practice

Bournville College of Further Education

Bournville College of Further Education in Birmingham has a good reputation for providing education for people with special needs. All the staff in their special needs unit are white. After an initial audit within the College, it was recognised that black and ethnic minority people with learning difficulties were greatly under-represented on some courses. In particular, the absence of Asian girls was noted as an issue of some concern.

Action plans have been initiated to take steps to redress the poor provision of further education services for black and ethnic minority people with learning difficulties within the College. Emphasis has been given to staff development and three areas have been identified for specific attention.

➣ **Monitoring** — Special needs students at the college are being monitored in order to elicit specific data about race and type of disability.

➣ **The College prospectus** — Looking at the way the prospectus is marketed to reflect the needs of a multicultural, multiracial society.

➣ **Developing community outreach** — To attract black and ethnic minority users and provide support to these groups.

Contact: Mrs Patricia Tyman, Principal
Or: Helen Gale, Senior Lecturer, Equal Opportunities (Race) Bournville College of Further Education, Bristol Road Birmingham B31 3AJ

Tel: 021 411 1414

As we have seen in Chapter 4, there are very few links between black and ethnic minority families and the education system. The links are even fewer when their "child" becomes an adult attending further education. The involvement of families in further education is not always positively encouraged or pursued in recognition of the student's adulthood, which in white families tends to mean the development of an identity separate from the family. For black and ethnic minority people, however, contact with families may be essential to building a holistic picture of the students themselves. The debate about individualism and more collective approaches to family life in different communities needs to be addressed.

It is possible that low participation in further education by black and ethnic minority people with learning difficulties reflects a lack of knowledge about opportunities, and families' perceptions of the courses offered as irrelevant to their relatives' needs. It is important that colleges adopt measures to address these issues and ensure greater access to further educational opportunities for young adults with learning difficulties from black and ethnic minority communities.

English as a Second Language

The problems confronting bilingual students with learning difficulties have been neglected by the education services. Often, little attention is given to the language which black and ethnic minority students speak at home.

As at school, education is predominantly (if not wholly) conducted in English. Thus many black and ethnic minority students with learning difficulties struggle in their language development, which may lead to confusion. Some teachers may recognise this as an area of concern but few initiatives have been established.

IDEAS IN PRACTICE

Spring Grove Centre

In September 1988, staff at Spring Grove Adult and Continuing Education Centre, Hounslow, became concerned that they knew very little about their bilingual students who came to them from Acton Lodge, a local Adult Training Centre (ATC). Staff did not know even which languages were spoken at home.

An action research project was established in which a bilingual worker liaised with staff at Acton Lodge, to gain more indepth knowledge about the students. They set out to:

➤ identify and establish contact with bilingual trainees

➤ look at provision made for them currently within the context of training/educational provision generally on offer

➤ examine, through direct contact, observation and liaison with care workers, the special educational needs of the "group" in the light of their language, competence and cultural background

➤ suggest possible strategies for effective support and development of "educational" work undertaken

➤ make recommendations for future developments

The project team worked with twelve students, establishing profiles of their lives. Languages spoken ranged from Punjabi, Gujerati, Hindi, Urdu.

The following recommendations were made to Spring Grove.

Short Term Strategies

➤ input from (a) multilingual tutor(s) to assist in the assessment process in future

➤ liaison between project worker and care workers to initiate support in structured activities as appropriate

➤ advice as/when required to be sought from multicultural and special needs advisers

➤ discussion to be initiated concerning allocation of trainees to groups where they might work together (e.g. groups of trainees with the same language/background)

Long Term Strategies

➤ on-going support for tutors and care workers to ensure an appropriate sensitivity to cultural diversity

➤ support for language development activities

➤ multilingual support for general training activities at the centre

➤ multilingual input into assessment and profiling of students

➤ establishment and development of links with the homes of black and ethnic minority students

Although it has not been possible to implement all the recommendations, they have raised awareness. The employment of bilingual staff is currently being advocated.

Contact: Tony Woodward
            Senior Organiser (Special Needs)
            Spring Grove
            Thornbury Road
            Isleworth
            Middlesex
            Tel: 081 569 8484

Adult Education

The potential contribution of adult/continuing education opportunities to the lives of people with learning difficulties is increasingly recognised. Many of the issues confronting black and ethnic minority students in adult education are similar to those encountered at school (Chapter 4) and in further education. Progress has been similarly slow in addressing questions of racial equality within adult education.

IDEAS IN PRACTICE

The National Institute of Adult Continuing Education (NIACE) points out that the participation of black and ethnic minority people in both the provision and take up of adult education is generally low. Recognising the lack of representation from black and ethnic minorities within its own structure, NIACE set up an Ethnic Minority Advisory Group to explore the Institute's constitution, organisational structure and procedures and to advise on ways of improving representation and participation by black and ethnic minority communities.

The Group found that institutional structures, policies and procedures often reflect the interests of the white majority community in terms of ethnicity, sex and class, and as a result work in ways that exclude other groups.

In response to these findings, and in the belief that all people must have real access to all areas of study, NIACE has made a commitment to equal opportunities. Its Equal Opportunities Policy commits NIACE to:

➢ seek explicitly to represent and to report on the full range of black and ethnic minority involvement in adult continuing education and to disseminate information on new initiatives and good practice in this respect

➢ review existing adult continuing education policies and provision to see how far they reflect the expressed needs and concerns of black people and ethnic minorities

➢ establish consultative procedures through which the views of black and ethnic minority people can be effectively represented

➢ recognise the value of developing initiatives in education for black and ethnic minority people and seek to support and encourage new ways of working in this area

➢ support and press for initiatives which increase black and ethnic minority participation and improve their position in adult continuing education as a whole

➢ draw attention to black and ethnic minority people's participation and contribution to the Institute and to the field via the regularly published newsletters and journals

Contact: NIACE
19B De Montfort Street
Leicester LE1 7HR
Tel: 0533 551451

IDEAS IN PRACTICE

The following examples have been taken from Jeannie Sutcliffe's handbook, *Adults with Learning Difficulties: Education for choice and empowerment* (Sutcliffe, 1990).

At **Newham Community College**, a course was run for black women with learning difficulties, tutored by two black women tutors. It examined the multiple oppressions experienced by the participants in terms of race, gender and disability. Time was given to consider various religions, music, foods and family backgrounds. Different cultures were celebrated, and positive images of black women were presented in pictures and books. The students developed in self esteem and identity and became more assertive — for instance, in requesting a course in dressmaking for Asian women.

The course was only funded for a short period. The co-ordinator is currently recommending that the provision should become an integral part of the college provision.

Contact: Sheila Mitchell
           Newham Community College
           West Ham Centre
           Welfare Road
           Stratford
           London E15
           Tel: 081 555 1422

At **Streatham and Tooting Adult Education Institute** the needs of students from different ethnic backgrounds are actively responded to. Students with learning difficulties have joined groups in "Black Studies" and in "Afro-Caribbean Cookery". Multicultural days are held where students can try on saris, taste different foods and participate in music and dance from other countries.

Contact: Bimba Karunaratna
           Broadwater Road
           Tooting Broadway
           London SW17
           Tel: 081 672 2683 cxt 12

In **Harrow**, English as a Second Language provision is offered to students with learning difficulties who want to improve their English.

For further information on developments in continuing education opportunities for adults with learning difficulties generally:

Contact: Jeannie Sutcliffe
           Charles Street Adult
              Education Centre
           Luton LU2 0EB
           Tel: 0582 22566

The options have limitations — Either an underpaid undervalued less secure and less pleasant job or an ATC place —

Adult education tutors need to assess the extent to which their courses are "culture bound". All too often, black and ethnic minority people with learning difficulties are expected to fit into the values and ideas expressed in courses, without having had any opportunity to influence their development. Staff should ensure that the courses provided are relevant to the lives of black and ethnic minority people with learning difficulties. For example:

➢ **Personal care** — Many people with learning difficulties attending adult education will need assistance with their personal care, which will vary according to cultural background. Routines of personal hygiene, washing and dressing vary. For example, if an Asian woman is wearing a sulwar kameez, do course workers know how to put on these clothes properly? Do they know how to teach the care of different types of hair and skin? (Personal care issues are discussed further on page 124.)

➢ **Life skills** — When teaching life skills, it is essential that tutors are aware of variations between cultures in social relationships. They should know the different social gatherings in which people participate and norms of appropriate behaviour. (To encourage some Asian women to socialise in mixed sex company may be inappropriate and unacceptable, for instance.) Tutors should find out what black and ethnic minority people value and find acceptable.

➢ **Dealing with racism** — Assertiveness training and confidence building are gaining in popularity in adult education. When working on such courses with black and ethnic minority students with learning difficulties, tutors must take account of the skills necessary to deal with the racism faced in their everyday lives.

ADULT TRAINING CENTRES

Adult Training Centres (ATCs) (otherwise known as Social Education Centres or Resource and Activity Centres) are the main form of daytime service provision open to people with learning difficulties after leaving school. In recent years it has been recognised that ATCs are not an ideal option, since students spend their time in a segregated situation alongside other people with learning difficulties often engaged in boring activities. However, since ATCs will continue for some time, it is important that ways are sought to ensure that they respond to the needs of *all* those who may wish to use them. A recent Social Services Inspectorate (SSI) survey showed that few black and ethnic minority people attend day centres, even in areas where there are substantial minority communities which could be expected to be a source of both staff and clients (SSI, 1989).

Our review of the literature, and more importantly, visits to centres and discussions with people with learning difficulties and their families, have confirmed that ATCs need to assess critically their appropriateness and accessibility for black and ethnic minority communities. Service providers need to establish whether:

➢ centres are based near to the communities they are serving

All too often black and ethnic minority people are placed in centres which isolate them from their own communities.

➢ organisers ensure that links are built up and maintained with local black and ethnic minority communities

For example, do they ensure that black and ethnic minority staff and volunteers are recruited? (See Chapter 7 on recruitment of black staff.)

➢ activities are designed so that those attending can find out about their local communities

For example, do they use their local shops while at the ATC, and are activities within the centre flexible enough to enable all people to benefit? Are single sex swimming and dancing sessions organised for those who may prefer them? Are the music, videos, posters and general decor of the centre multiracial in nature?

➢ food preferences of users from black and ethnic minority communities are catered for

In a study in Nottingham, the most frequent complaint people had about ATCs was about inappropriate food — especially the lack of halal meat on menus (Nottingham Social Services Dept., 1987).

➢ there is provision to ensure that people with learning difficulties whose mother tongue is not English have full access to the services of the centre

Are people encouraged to speak in their mother tongue? Are bilingual staff employed?

➢ procedures such as Individual Programme Plans take full account of the experiences, circumstances and wishes of black and ethnic minority families

A Coventry survey showed that people's cultural needs were not taken into account during review meetings. It was recommended that an interpreter should be available at reviews if necessary and that there should be more outreach work with parents (Cocking and Athwal, 1990).

Towards Better Practice

The SSI report cited one or two encouraging examples of authorities which had tried to address these issues. One London borough with a substantial ethnic minority population had adopted authority-wide policies on race which were to be reflected in each department's activities. The social services department had appointed staff from relevant backgrounds with a specific responsibility for minority clients' requirements. One unit had

---

IDEAS IN PRACTICE

Lanercost Resource and Activity Centre

Lanercost RAC is an Adult Training Centre in Bristol. It is fairly isolated from local black and ethnic minority communities. Nevertheless, 10% of the Centre's students are from black and ethnic minority groups. Since the recent appointment of a black manager, students have been encouraged and supported to pursue activities in their own areas. By using local facilities they are beginning to find out about, and build links within, their own communities.

Further changes have been made to ensure that the environment of the Centre reflects the cultural and racial background of students (for example, by putting up posters showing black people as well as white).

The Centre has also supported the development of a black students' group, which meets together and shares common concerns. Such initiatives have enabled black and ethnic minority people with learning difficulties to overcome some of their isolation and have made their activities at the Centre more relevant to their lifestyles.

Contact: Sue Jenkins
           Lanercost Resource and
               Activity Centre
           Lanercost Road
           Southmead
           Bristol BS10 6HZ
           Tel: 0272 503544

Derbyshire Social Services

Derbyshire Social Services Department has employed four instructors from Afro-Caribbean and Asian backgrounds to work specifically with people with learning difficulties from their own ethnic origin in ATCs.

Apart from their language and cultural skills, the workers pay special attention to making the centres more reflective of the users' backgrounds. Particular emphasis has been given to building links with the local black and ethnic minority communities. In one case this has led to setting up a support group for parents.

Contact: Parmajit Oberoi
           Derbyshire County Council
           County Offices
           Matlock
           Derbyshire
           Tel: 0629 580000

Ideas In Practice

Whetley Hill Asian Ladies Group, Bradford

Whetley Hill Asian Ladies Group is run by Bradford Social Services Department specifically for disabled Asian women. The group was originally set up by volunteers because there were no facilities to meet the needs of disabled Asian women as a separate group. Mixed groups of men and women do not generally meet together in the local Asian community. A group of workers from Social and Health Services and from the voluntary sector collaborated to plan support which took into account the dietary, cultural and religious requirements of the women.

The group now has a regular membership of 12 women, aged 16–65, who attend Whetley Hill Day Centre every Monday. Transport is provided and support is given by a group of women staff, including interpreters.

During the day, the women take part in activities such as reading and educational activities, sewing, knitting and embroidery. Shopping expeditions, trips to the park and days out are also organised. They are encouraged to bring in their own home videos of weddings and films sent to them from Pakistan. The women also participate in planning, purchasing and cooking their lunches each week. Some women are learning to design their own clothes with the help of a representative from Fashion Services for the Disabled.

The then Principal Officer for Services to the Handicapped and Disabled, Miss Irene Senior, said:

The aim of the group is to help families get a break from their full time jobs of caring for the ladies. And it gives the ladies a chance to learn new skills, become more independent and confident in their lives. It is a very happy and interesting group and we are hoping that we can encourage more members of the Asian community to take advantage of this very special service, which they deserve.

Contact: Farida Sheik or Richard Jefferson
Whetley Hill Resource Centre
3 Whetley Hill
Bradford BD8 8LN
Tel: 0274 495442

For a first-hand account of how one member of staff tried to improve services for black and ethnic minority people attending the Centre where she worked, see Chapter 8, page 187.

organised weeks during which all trainees were introduced to food, music and leisure activities of a particular culture. Activities and equipment such as wall posters and jigsaws reflected their multiracial clientele. However, in contrast to this positive example, the SSI frequently came across instances where no consideration was given to the needs of black and ethnic minority clients if there were only one or two of them (SSI, 1989).

Occupational Therapy and "Training for Independence"

For some people living in hospital, occupational therapy may be the main daytime activity available. It is important that occupational therapists (whether community or hospital based) ensure their work reflects the multiracial society in which they practise. Are the kinds of art and craft activities on offer appropriate to *all* individuals, whatever their background? Do the decor and decorations (e.g. pictures and posters) in the occupational therapy department reflect a multiracial world? Are the materials, tools and materials used for teaching (e.g. cooking utensils and ingredients) relevant to the lifestyles of black and ethnic minority clients?

It is common practice — in occupational therapy, ATCs and elsewhere — to teach people with learning difficulties to prepare English/European style snack foods as part of their "training for independent living". We were told of one Asian young man who seemed to be unexpectedly slow in mastering the preparation of baked beans on toast. Further enquiries revealed that he was quite adept at making a simple vegetable curry — but was clearly not interested in learning to cook unfamiliar food which was irrelevant to his lifestyle at home.

EMPLOYMENT

Employment is a valued aspect of life in Britain. Paid employment means more money, access to friends, a potentially more fulfilling life and a recognised role in the community (King's Fund Centre, 1984). For many, paid employment is the block upon which the rest of their life is built.

Historically, people with learning difficulties have been denied access to paid employment. On leaving school, they have an extremely limited range of options. They may go to an ATC, or stay at home, or possibly go on to further education. Few go into paid work. People with learning difficulties are mainly restricted to welfare alternatives which constrain their experiences and keep them segregated. As a result, their economic and other resources may be limited.

Black and ethnic minority people with learning difficulties, and those helping to support them, face multiple challenges in the search for employment.

Black and ethnic minority people in this country are largely concentrated in those areas of work which are unpopular and low paid. The majority are in manual jobs, particularly semi-skilled and unskilled manual work. Overall, black and ethnic minority men earn substantially less than white men (Brown, 1984). This is due in part to their concentration at lower job levels, but also because within each socio-economic category there are clear inequalities between the earnings of black and white men.

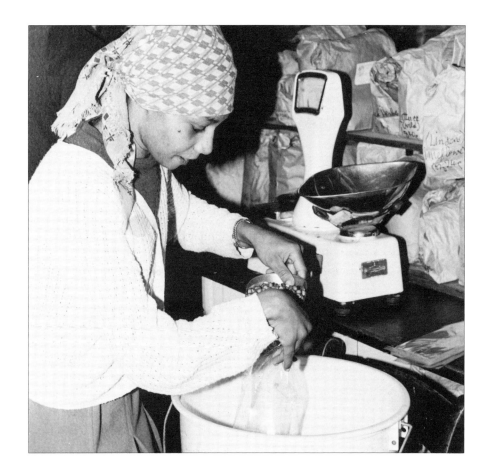

Unemployment amongst black and ethnic minority groups is double that for white people (Huhne, 1989). They are particularly vulnerable to unemployment because a high proportion used to work in jobs and industries which have been most affected by recession: in manual jobs, in the private sector, in industrial manufacture, and particularly in the textile and clothing industries. Black school leavers and young adults are particularly badly affected. Discrimination is still a major feature of their experiences in the labour market.

A study by the Policy Studies Institute (Brown and Jay, 1985) found that one third of private employers discriminated against Asians and Afro-Caribbeans by refusing them an interview which they would have offered to equally qualified and experienced white applicants. A recent report suggests that these trends in the labour market have not improved (Brown, 1990).

People with learning difficulties need support to work in a competitive economic environment where their needs are rarely taken into consideration. For black people with learning difficulties — facing the double discrimination of handicap and race — the need for support is all the more acute. Linking an "advocate" to an individual with learning difficulties may help to ensure that that person's needs and interests are

IDEAS IN PRACTICE

ASRA Disability Employment Project, Southall

Rupen Chande is employed by ASRA Ltd to work specifically with Asian people with mental health problems, disabilities or learning difficulties, and help them to pursue training and part or full time employment opportunities. Staff at ASRA will help people apply for jobs and assist with preparation for interviews and in associated areas like benefits.

Contact: Rupen Chande
ASRA Disability Employment
Project
Windmill Centre
2–4 Windmill Lane
Southall
Middlesex UB2 4NJ

Tel: 081 574 7644

The Pathway Employment Service

The Pathway Employment Service was established by MENCAP to increase employment opportunities available to people with learning difficulties. The project gives information about benefits, job trials and grant help to employers and fellow support workers in the workplace during job trial and training periods.

Contact: The Royal Society for Mentally
Handicapped Children and
Adults (MENCAP)
Pathway Employment Service
169a City Road
Cardiff CF2 3JB

Tel: 0222 482072

Workshops on Disability, Pathway Project, Southall

Pathway Further Education Centre in Southall has run workshops for people working in a supportive role with black disabled people.

The aims of the workshops were to:

➤ examine specific disabilities and their effects on disabled people

➤ examine services available for black disabled people

➤ explore negative attitudes towards disabilities and look at ways of challenging them

➤ bring a group of workers together to share experience and expertise in working with disabled people

➤ consider the role of self-advocacy and user involvement in planning services

(This project was funded for the short term only and has now closed down.)

Contact: Pathway Further Education Centre
Havelock Road
Southall
Middlesex

Tel: 081 571 2241

promoted, both in seeking employment and in the workplace. Issues raised by advocacy with black and ethnic minority people are discussed later in this chapter (page 141).

It is important that black and ethnic minority people have opportunities of employment in their own communities. This will encourage feelings of belonging and of playing a useful role. Helpful strategies include:

➢ seeking out potential employers (including those who are themselves from black and ethnic minority communities)

➢ identifying support colleagues at the workplace (ideally perhaps from the same community as the individual concerned)

Some voluntary and statutory organisations have begun to develop employment opportunities for people with learning difficulties. However, progress has been slower in responding to the challenge of both race and employment in this area.

RESIDENTIAL SERVICES

Ethnic minority communities are almost without exception particularly ill-served by the residential sector.

RESIDENTIAL CARE: A POSITIVE CHOICE (THE WAGNER REPORT, 1988)

Residential care needs of black people should not be viewed as special …
The special needs factor perpetuates a situation of "them" and "us" which is unhelpful towards promoting equality …

Respect for the individual as a philosophy is a good base to start from. Wagner states that "caring is about treating people individually; thus a residential establishment where individuality is respected at all times and in all circumstances is by definition a caring one" …

(NZIRA, 1989)

Meeting Individual Needs

The regime of care provided by most residential establishments for people with learning difficulties reflects the norms and practices of the majority white population. Residential care routines need to be reviewed to ensure that they meet the needs of *all* their residents — including black and ethnic minority residents — in ways that are appropriate and acceptable to them and their families.

IDEAS IN PRACTICE

Personal Care Resource Pack — Riverside Health Authority

A group of black homecare managers are in the process of developing a resource pack, designed for residential staff working with black service users. It will provide basic information on hair, skin care, foods and diet and will also include a directory of useful local hairdressers, shops and restaurants.

The pack will take the form of a video and supporting booklets to:

➤ demonstrate techniques and methods for grooming hair, caring for skin and preparing meals

➤ give information about types of hair, skin and food products and their availability

The initiative is funded by the Health Authority.

Contact: Judy Miller, Sonia Simon,
Joan Sterling
20 Kingsbridge Road
London W10
Tel: 081 960 0995

➤ **Personal care** — White staff and carers often do not take adequate personal care of the black and ethnic minority people with learning difficulties living in the establishments within which they work. This reflects inadequate training for work in a multicultural, multiracial society. With little in-service training in these matters, their knowledge of personal care is limited to their own experience.

Personal hygiene and care routines will differ between cultural backgrounds. To ensure respect for individuals and to avoid damaging practices and confusion, staff and carers should follow personal care and hygiene routines adopted at home. Although individual families will differ from each other, some general points may serve as a useful starting point from which to explore and adopt appropriate practices.

— People may prefer a carer of the same sex, especially when bathing and attending to hygiene needs.

— Asian people may prefer to wash themselves after going to the toilet. Not to do so would be highly offensive.

— Some people may prefer to use their left hand for carrying out cleaning functions and the right hand for handling food, greeting and dealing with people.

➤ **Skin and hair care** — Staff need to be aware that people from black and ethnic minority communities have different needs and preferences when taking care of their skin and hair.

— Service providers should be careful not to use pink skin as the norm. They should be able to recognise important changes in darker skin, such as bruising, other forms of injury and jaundice.

— Darker skin may need more moisturising. This is particularly important after activities such as swimming.

— Kinky hair often needs more moisturising than straight hair, especially after washing. Combing through is important to prevent the hair from becoming matted. The appropriate comb and hair products should be used to avoid discomfort and damage to the hair.

— It is important that people's preferences are established for how their hair should be arranged. For example, Sikh children, including boys, may want their hair plaited and/or tied in a top knot. People with kinky hair will also have their own way of combing and styling.

➤ **Food** — Catering arrangements should ensure that there is a choice of menus to suit individual preferences. Vegetarians should be catered for and halal meals should be available for those people requiring them.

➤ **Religion** — People's religious wishes should be respected and facilitated. Some hospitals or hostels make arrangements for people to go home, or for the whole family to visit, on religious days or other special festivals or holidays.

➤ **Daytime activities** — These should be relevant to, and reflect, the interests and everyday lives of black and ethnic minority people.

➤ **Positive images of black and ethnic minority people** — Such images should be portrayed in residential settings. Posters, pictures, books and toys should be multiracial. Golliwogs and books like "Little Black Sambo" which offend black and ethnic minority people should not be available. (For children, a variety of dolls of all ethnic origins are now available.)

➤ **Home liaison** — Liaison with black and ethnic minority families and communities is important (see Chapter 4). Black and ethnic minority families may find it difficult to relate to an institution which embodies white Anglo-Saxon values, and may not appear to take their needs into account.

➤ **Visiting** — For some communities, visiting relatives in hospital (or other residential accommodation) may be viewed as a social responsibility and a social occasion. It is not uncommon for a wide range of family members, relatives and friends to visit in groups. This may conflict with the norms of the white community or the hospital where visiting is restricted to next of kin and close relatives. It is important that black and ethnic minority families are not made to feel unwelcome because of different norms and practices regarding visiting. On the other hand, relatives of some black and ethnic minority residents may not be able to visit often if they live far away. Staff should be careful not to assume that these families do not care about their relatives. Attempts should be made to enable and encourage visiting wherever possible.

Racism in Residential Services

What remains a worry for many black people is the growing documentation of the racism inherent in the authorities and institutions involved in service delivery. To imagine that there were no manifestations of racism within residential care would be unproductive. So a frank acknowledgement of the reality of racist attitudes can offer hope to black people in need of residential care. Once acknowledged, racism must be challenged because it is wrong and an unacceptable form of behaviour that interferes with people's ability to provide genuine care ... The message to all who choose to care for others is that, unless their actions are guided by a sense of importance of every human being, their competence and professionalism will remain questionable.

(NZIRA, 1989)

The skills and perspectives of black staff are essential in providing antiracist and multiracial services. Black and ethnic minority staff are, however, usually in the lower echelons of services and are therefore excluded from

---

Residential Homes for Black and Ethnic Minority People with Learning Difficulties: A Checklist for Better Practice

➤ Is the home located in a multiracial neighbourhood, with other black and ethnic minority people living nearby?

➤ Is the staff group multiracial? Are there any black or ethnic minority staff in management positions?

➤ Does the home have an equal opportunities policy? Is it implemented in practice?

➤ Is there a complaints procedure to handle instances of racial discrimination, abuse or harassment? Is it used? Do staff and residents know that such incidents will be taken seriously and dealt with effectively?

➤ Are links fostered between individual residents and local facilities and networks of interest to them? For example, social centres, places of worship etc.

➤ Are personal/cultural preferences regarding client, personal care, clothing, activites, religious observance, routinely and readily met?

➤ Are individuals treated with dignity and respect, in accordance with their own and their family's wishes, taking account of their sex, age and ethnic, religious and cultural identity?

---

decision making. Efforts must be made to ensure that black staff are present at every level of residential care services. This can be achieved by adoption and implementation of equal opportunities policies (see Chapter 7, Black and Ethnic Minority Staff). Effective complaints procedures must be introduced in residential establishments to deal with racial discrimination wherever it occurs.

Carers' Views on Residential Provision

Most black and ethnic minority children and adults with learning difficulties live at home with their families.

A report from Nottingham Social Services Department (1987) based on interviews with a number of carers from ethnic minority communities in the city revealed the following.

➤ When asked to choose what type of residential provision they would prefer if arrangements with the extended family did not work out, most carers mentioned more than one possible alternative. The majority (65%) envisaged future care being provided either by the extended family or within the current family home; 38% would not contemplate any other option.

➤ Where respondents were prepared to consider alternative accommodation, group homes were the most popular option.

➤ Fostering and local authority hostel provision were least popular.

In many cases people expressed the desire for schemes which allowed individuals with learning difficulties to live with others from the same ethnic, cultural and religious background.

Carers would prefer a black home — feel X would identify greatly with others.
Feels X would have to choose for himself.
Wouldn't mind group home being mixed race. X is used to this sort of setting.

AFRO-CARIBBEAN CARERS

Ideally will stay with his sisters, but failing that with a Pakistani foster family.
Same ethnic group (Pakistani). Trans-racial placements only for a few weeks.
Fostering by same race family.
Parents would like group home staffed with Asians, but with people of similar ability is essential.
Don't mind who he lives with, but religion and culture to be taken into account and provided for.
No transracial placements.

ASIAN CARERS

Life Sharing and Residential Services for Black People with Learning Difficulties

Life sharing involves recruiting a person or people to live in the home of a person or people with learning difficulties. Life sharers are engaged on a specific contract basis for at least a year.

This approach is in its infancy and has achieved some degree of success in Clwyd, Wales. Graham Harper, County Development Officer and Principal Officer for services to people with learning difficulties in Clwyd says life sharing means far more than just sharing accommodation. The life sharer is expected to involve the individual with learning difficulties in their whole way of life. Clearly, sustaining a relationship of rich intensity is not without stress (Harper, 1989).

A life sharer in effect becomes part of the family of the person with learning difficulties. Feeling part of a family is instrumental in giving people a sense of "who" they are. Family members usually share many of the same values, activities and culture. For black and ethnic minority people this bond can be strengthened by encouraging and enabling them to maintain aspects of their family lifestyle, for example food, dress, religious customs, supporting them in traditional family celebrations such as anniversaries, Barmitzvah, birthdays, Chanukah, Christmas and New Year, Christenings, Eid, Divali, funerals and weddings.

If black and ethnic minority people with learning difficulties are to be treated with respect and dignity, then race and cultural dimensions must be taken on board. This will have implications for recruitment programmes which must be geared towards attracting staff from all sections of the community.

On the basis of their specially commissioned study, Integrate decided to:

➤ take special steps to find out about groups and individuals with special needs within the ethnic minority groups, and any special housing and support requirements

➤ take these needs into account when planning priorities

➤ take special steps to ensure that people from ethnic minorities know about and are encouraged to apply for special needs provision

Integrate have recommended that:

➤ all special needs provision should take into consideration the linguistic and cultural diversity in society and recognise the different needs of ethnic minority groups

➤ any needs assessment and referral of nomination procedures should ensure that such groups are not inadvertently excluded from any provision

➤ in some cases it may be appropriate to employ bilingual support workers

(BRAILEY ET AL, 1989)

Contact: Integrate
58 Fox Street
Glasgow G1 4AU
Tel: 041 204 3311

Private and Independent Sector Housing

An increasing number of housing associations now run homes for people with learning difficulties. However, several organisations we contacted, including the National Federation of Housing Associations, were concerned that few black people are referred to these projects.

A study commissioned by Integrate, a Glasgow special housing group (Cranny, 1988), revealed that:

➤ the key statutory agencies (Glasgow District Council, Strathclyde Regional Council and Greater Glasgow Health Board) did not keep ethnic records to enable the specific needs for services to people from ethnic minorities to be monitored

➤ knowledge of special needs housing among ethnic minorities ranged from "poor" to "non-existent"

➤ existing support services were seen as largely inappropriate (e.g. meals on wheels only providing European style meals)

Black Housing Associations

Black housing associations have been established by black and ethnic minority communities in response to the discrimination they face in obtaining suitable housing. Recently, however, they have been particularly badly affected by cash crises at the Housing Corporation. With few financial reserves, they cannot afford to pay up-front for building land and recoup the cost later from the Corporation. These housing associations cater increasingly for people with special needs, such as the elderly and the homeless, but progress in the area of learning difficulties is slow. Limited dialogue between black and ethnic minority communities and local and health authorities is one reason that black housing associations have not yet begun to respond to the housing needs of people with learning difficulties. In the future, local and health authorities will have a responsibility to contract out services to the private and independent sector. It is important that steps are taken to ensure that black and ethnic minority communities are consulted and informed about the needs of black and ethnic minority people with learning difficulties in their area.

Private Residential Homes

Private residential homes are playing an increasing role in providing accommodation and support to people with learning difficulties. Many will not have had much opportunity to think about the needs of people from black and ethnic minority communities. A few cater specifically for black and ethnic minority people with learning difficulties. The Asian proprietor of one home (who had previously worked as a nurse) told us that he had established his home out of concerns that:

➢ Asian people in residential provision were losing out on the "Asian living" experience of having relatives, cousins and other family members around

➢ they also missed out on visits to religious places and on celebrations of important religious events

➢ they were not spending time with other people who spoke their own language

He felt that in their new home they could:

➢ enjoy cooking Indian food without fear of negative comments

➢ watch Indian films

➢ enhance domestic skills rather than "socialising" and eating out in pubs and restaurants

➢ not be taunted and racially abused by name calling

➢ now value and celebrate the fact that they are Indian which will enhance their own self image and identity

Personal Relationships, Leisure and Recreation

Most adults have a variety of relationships. These "ties and connections" (King's Fund Centre, 1988) give them a sense of belonging. People with learning difficulties, however (even those living in a house in a community setting), may still lack opportunities to develop relationships and pursue the leisure and recreation activities of their choice. Where efforts are made to enable people with learning difficulties to develop social activities and relationships, ideas of how to proceed are inevitably based upon a white British way of life. In Britain, personal relationships tend to develop at the individual level, whereas in many ethnic minority communities social interactions focus on collective and family life.

White staff and carers must, therefore, review their own assumptions of what is "normal" and "desirable". They should always clarify with the black and ethnic minority people with whom they are involved what they consider to be "normal", valued or accepted behaviour and activities, and should be alert to any relevant cultural issues or practices. At the same time, staff must also be careful to avoid subscribing to stereotyped views of what is "normal" for a particular community group. Individuals and families vary.

Friendship

Most people with learning difficulties, whether living at home with parents or in institutions, have few friends (Richardson and Ritchie, 1989). Often, they will need the support of someone who can provide them with a "way in" to existing networks, organisations and activities and who can support their involvement in these — with the possibility that opportunities for friendship may develop in due course.

Some black and ethnic minority people may have additional difficulties in making friends. Low self-esteem, and the fear of prejudice and rejection, may deter them from even trying. This is made worse if they are the only black person in a social situation and are, therefore, made to feel different. Helping someone to become involved in the networks and organisations of their own community will avoid this particular problem.

Asian Women

The perceived position of Asian women within their cultures often leads to their being stereotyped as submissive, shy and introvert. This can influence the way in which service providers interpret Asian women's personal needs and the appropriate action taken to meet them. Alternatively, Asian women may be inappropriately encouraged to adopt the leisure activities of their white counterparts. They may, for example, be encouraged to go to a pub,

Harinder's Story

Harinder is a young Asian man with Down's Syndrome. He lives at home with his parents and other brothers and sisters. He is from a Sikh family and he participates in all the activities of the gurdwara (Sikh temple). Harinder attends regularly, particularly on Sundays when he has the responsibility of being the shoe attendant. He collects the shoes and gives people their tickets. He also helps out with the food and enjoys the social life of the gurdwara.

or club, or go out with boys. If "messages" given by the services they use (school, residential home or ATC) differ from the norms of their own communities, great confusion and distress may result for them and their families.

Of course, ideas of what is normal, valued or desirable will differ between individuals and families within the same cultural group. Staff must be careful, therefore, to be sensitive to clients' cultural identity while avoiding the trap of making blanket assumptions about what "Asian women" do or want in life. When in doubt, check it out with those directly concerned.

Cultural and Religious Life

Black and ethnic minority people with learning difficulties want to get involved in their own communities' organisations and activities. However, staff from a different background may not readily find out about, or show an interest in, these activities. For example, Asian weddings can be major social occasions. Often festivities last over a period of days. This period is a time for meeting new people and strengthening personal relationships. White service providers should be aware of this, and prepared to encourage their Asian service users to participate.

Within many black and ethnic minority communities, religion may have a big influence on people's everyday life. Migration often strengthens religious beliefs, affiliations and ties. For many, a place of worship is somewhere to channel their energies, where they no longer feel alienated and excluded.

Afro-Caribbean churches have been a source of support to many in this community. It is here that some people learn to speak in public. This helps them to overcome feelings of fear, inferiority and selfconsciousness and to build up courage and self confidence.

Mr Cohen and Mr Joseph

Mr Cohen and Mr Joseph lived for many years in Darenth Park Hospital in Dartford — which is not an area renowned for its strong Jewish community! When the resettlement team first met him, Mr Cohen told us he wanted to live with other Jews. Mr Joseph did not tell us that he was Jewish, but responded very enthusiastically when I learnt that he was Jewish, and wished him a Happy Chanukah (it was that time of year). Before this, we had not really been able to interest Mr Joseph in anything other than his cigarettes. But he very much enjoyed talking about Jewish subjects, and we were very impressed by how much he remembered from the times (decades ago) when he had been active as a Jew.

I saw how important their Jewish identity was to both men. I also recognised how completely neglected were the religious and cultural needs of other Jews in the hospital. So I organised various events such as festival celebrations in the hospital. (I am myself Jewish and this helped with knowing what to do, when and how!) We also visited Jewish museums together and enjoyed other activities such as reading bible stories and watching "Jewish videos".

Before we could arrange for Mr Cohen to live somewhere with other Jews, a friend of his asked him to move into the next door flat in a (Christian) sheltered housing scheme. Luckily South London has a small but active Jewish community and Mr Cohen could choose which of the two synagogues he wanted to join. He also joined two local day centres for Jewish old people, and once a week schlepped up to the much larger Sobell day centre in North London.

In addition to the regular activities available at the Sobell centre, Mr Cohen is able to join in special occasions. So he will be going with a helper next year on the centre's two-week holiday to Israel.

We are in the process of working with Redbridge Social Services to find a Jewish family with whom Mr Joseph can live. (Redbridge has the benefit of being the largest Jewish community in Europe, as well as being nearer Mr Joseph's family.) The local Jewish community centre has said they will be pleased to have him as a daily member.

(FROM JANNER, 1988–9)

Churches supply black women with one of our main sources of support and sustenance, offering some continuity with the forms of social and community organisation we had known in the Caribbean ... For many it is the only form of recreation.

(BRYAN ET AL, 1985)

An Afro-Caribbean nurse told us:

I first met Sister Scaffe in church which she has regularly attended for many years. Although in her late fifties and unable to read or write, she is an active, enthusiastic and hardworking member who has a particular interest in things that concern women. She also sings in the choir. Sister Scaffe often stands up to "testify her faith" to the congregation. She is a valuable member who obviously knows she "belongs".

It is only lately when I began to take an interest in people with learning difficulties that it became obvious to me that Sister Scaffe could be classified as someone who had a learning difficulty.

For several participants at the "Sharing Experiences" conference (see page 146), religion provided a sense of strength and belonging (Baxter, 1990a). They were confident and spoke often about other church sisters and brothers. They took a keen interest in their personal appearance and were sociable.

One thing which several of them had in common was that they had spent their early years in the Caribbean where they participated fully in the life of the community.

Sister Scaffe grew up in Jamaica. When she was in her late thirties her mother died and she came to live here with her younger sister. She had a normal life in Jamaica, including being active in the church. She worked in a variety of casual jobs and continued to do so on her arrival in Britain twenty years ago. Because her childhood was spent in the Caribbean, Sister Scaffe had completely escaped the label of being mentally handicapped. With her main focus being the church, she now lives the normal life of a retired woman in the Afro-Caribbean community.

Afro-Caribbean Nurse

In Britain, religion is no longer of great significance to the majority of white people. It is particularly important, therefore, that (white) service providers are sensitive to the religious and spiritual needs of those they support. Conscious effort must be made to ensure that services do not isolate people from their religion. People with learning difficulties from black and ethnic minority communities should be positively supported to maintain this aspect of their community life.

Those involved in the support and care of people with learning difficulties should be able and willing to embrace the spiritual aspects of people's lives. (White) staff and carers need to ask themselves:

➢ What are my feelings about religion?

➢ What are my views and knowledge about religions other than Christianity?

➢ Would I be able to give spiritual comfort to someone if they asked for it?

➢ How would I feel about accompanying someone to a gurdwara, mosque or pentecostal church?

Ideas In Practice

Asian People with Disability Alliance (APDA)

APDA aims to provide social, cultural and recreational activities for disabled Asians which are currently not being met.

The organisation also aims to provide information on welfare rights and services, employment opportunities, education and training in accessible forms of communication, including the relevant Asian languages.

APDA hopes to provide Respite Care or Give Mum a Break. They also hope to open centres where training, advice and information on dealing with the problems associated with disabled people are easily available.

It is a non-religious, non-political organisation, struggling to manage on a relatively small pump-priming grant of about £20,000.

Contact: Michael Jiwa
105a Melville Road
Stonebridge
London NW10

Tel: 081 965 3860

Outreach

Outreach is a Jewish voluntary organisation and registered charity working primarily with Jewish people, but also those of other denominations who have special needs. The purpose is to promote the integration and participation of mentally handicapped adults and young people within the Jewish and wider community.

Whilst providing information and support to families, counselling relief, respite and opportunities for volunteering, the emphasis is on self-advocacy.

Outreach offers a leisure integration programme designed to provide opportunities to experience and participate in a range of social activities, holiday programmes and educational opportunities. In conjunction with Greater Manchester Jewish Housing Association, a Residential Training facility is designed to equip people to live more independently.

Schemes are based mainly in the Crumpsall area of North Manchester, Salford and Prestwich. Each of these areas has access to a synagogue, kosher food shops and other cultural and religious amenities.

The organisation receives funds from the local authority and from the health authority resettlement programme.

Contact: Paul Sutton
Outreach Residential Services
24a Bury New Road
Manchester M25 8LD

Tel: 061 798 0180

IDEAS IN PRACTICE

Single Sex Swimming Classes in Hulme, Manchester

Women-only swimming classes, particularly welcoming to Asian women, have been arranged in Hulme, Manchester. Boys over 12 years and men are not allowed into the pool during classes. Women are able to swim in whatever makes them feel most comfortable and may enter the water fully clothed.

Leisure and Recreation

Local recreational facilities may not always reflect the full range of leisure preferences existing within a multiracial society. For example, swimming is a fairly cheap, accessible and acceptable form of recreation which is also valued for its therapeutic qualities. However, swimwear regulations and mixed sex swimming at local baths and swimming pools may exclude women whose cultural beliefs include principles of modesty. The same is true for going out to the pub for a drink. Some people from black and ethnic minority communities may not view this as a desirable pastime (particularly if alcohol is not part of their social and cultural norms).

Libraries

Many libraries will not have reading material, pictures and decor which positively represent the range of local communities, cultures and interests. Local authorities with equal opportunity units and race and disability officers may, however, offer better facilities.

IDEAS IN PRACTICE

The City of Manchester has an equal opportunities co-ordinator for its libraries. Longsight Library serves a richly diverse multiracial community, and has a librarian responsible for liaising with black and ethnic minority communities, finding out about relevant materials and networks. In addition, the library stocks books and tapes in five Asian languages, and for children there are a variety of dual language books. There are similar resources for the Afro-Caribbean communities.

The library also liaises with all the schools (including special schools) in the area. Children with learning difficulties visit the library with their teachers. Staff then expect them and are around to assist. In addition, the children are encouraged to visit on their own whenever they like. Similar arrangements exist in other areas with local ATCs.

EASY READING MATERIALS

The following books and packs suitable for people with learning difficulties are multiracial and multicultural in content.

Bedford Special Adult Learning Programmes
(Kulwinder Series)
Westbourne Centre
Westbourne Road
Bedford

Forest Readers
Berridge Centre
Berridge Road
Forest Fields
Nottingham N67 6HW

Rocky Books
Handprint Basic Readers
Unit 4
137 Soho Road
Birmingham B21 9SC

At Home in Britain:
Resource Pack for English as a Second Language
National Extension College
18 Brooklands Avenue
Cambridge CB2 2HN

Socialising Pack: Eating Out, Cooking a Meal
LDA (Learning Development Awareness)
Duke Street
Wisbech
Cambridgeshire PE13 2AE

English as a Second Language Resources
(including maternity language course, the Bassi and Ali series; the Brudenell series)
PRU Publications
Leeds City Council
27 Harrogate Road
Leeds LS7 3PD

A directory of easy-reading materials for adults with learning difficulties is to be published in November 1990 under the title *Read Easy* (Marshall and Porter, 1990).

For further information, contact:

Margaret Marshall
6A Harmer Green Lane
Digswell, Welwyn
Herts AL6 0AD

Tel: 043 871 6020

Sexuality

The sexual development, expression and relationships of people with learning difficulties have, historically, been suppressed and strictly controlled. It is an area that has been steeped in ambivalent attitudes and negative stereotypes (Craft, 1987). For many people, even today, the sexuality of individuals with learning difficulties is a sensitive and controversial subject. Recently, however, in keeping with the movement towards respecting the equal rights and needs of people with learning difficulties, it has received more attention. But little thought has been given to the particular needs of black and ethnic minority people with learning difficulties. They will face double discrimination because of the purportedly stronger sexual drives of black people generally — stereotypes already held about people with learning difficulties anyway (Baxter, 1990b).

There are very few books, articles or resources on this issue which incorporate a multiracial/multicultural perspective. A review of models of multicultural sex education (Compton, 1989) highlights their cultural insensitivity, particularly to Muslims, and asks whether therapists and health educators perpetuate inappropriate approaches in discussion and treatment of sexuality with students and clients.

It is important that staff are sensitive to the personal/sexual needs and expectations of the black and ethnic minority people with whom they work and their families — and are aware of the stereotypes which ethnic minority people may fear will be applied to them. Since little attention has been paid to this issue, teaching resources and sex education programmes do not reflect the values and experiences of black and ethnic minority people. Many of the ideas presented through sex education are based around the norm of a white nuclear family which excludes other types of family life and sex roles within them.

Marriage

In Britain marriage for people with learning difficulties has only recently become more accepted. Even now, there can still be great resistance from professionals, even though research has shown that couples may cope well, and live together happily (Mattinson, 1975; Craft and Craft, 1979).

Resistance to marriage for people with learning difficulties may not be the case in some Asian families. For many Asian families marriage will be an important expectation for all individuals. Whilst recognising the difficulties posed by having a handicap, there may not be the same underlying taboos

Calville and Beatrice

Calville, a 34 year old Afro-Caribbean man with mild learning difficulties has been involved in a relationship with a white woman, Beatrice, for some months. He lives in a hostel and finds that life there is not supportive of his relationship. His self-respect is continually being undermined by staff and the institution's regime. Beatrice is not allowed to come into his room, yet he says he has no money to take her out. Besides these difficulties (which he has in common with many other people) he is also facing personal racism due to his relationship with a white woman. He says people have asked "Why are you going out with her?" Beatrice's family have also made it clear to them that they don't approve. She has been told to stop going out with him.

Pauline

Pauline, an Afro-Caribbean woman lives in a hostel. It is an all-white environment where she has had little contact with other black people. The staff are all white and have made no attempt to provide a black perspective to hostel life. Pauline has a strong relationship with a white man and they intend to get married. However, their relationship has not been supported by professionals who view their plans to get married negatively.

concerning matrimony, and efforts may be made to allow marriage to take place. Such expectations by Asian parents are often construed by white health professionals as being "over optimistic" and "unrealistic". For example, one Muslim father's views that the special school attended by his daughter with moderate learning difficulties should teach his daughter "how to be a good wife" were seen both as limiting and unrealistic.

When people are confronted with mixed race relationships, a host of feelings emerge and may manifest themselves in a denial of the relationships' viability. The result may be that these relationships receive little support. The individuals concerned may lose confidence in themselves and the relationship (see box above).

Advocacy

Advocacy is based on the premise that the relationship between service users and service providers is not equal and works to the detriment of the service user. It is hard for people with learning difficulties to negotiate what happens to them and what kind of care and support they will receive. They frequently need others with more powerful voices to stand up with them and lend their influence.

Advocacy involves speaking up for, and supporting, a person or issue to the benefit of the individual or groups of individuals concerned. Several forms of advocacy are necessary and important to safeguard the interests of people with learning difficulties.

Citizen Advocacy

Within the field of learning difficulties, citizen advocacy schemes have emerged as a way in which a private citizen can befriend an individual on a one-to-one basis and defend their interests, on a voluntary basis without pay. The aim is to assist the person with learning difficulties to obtain their full rights and entitlements and a better quality of life. Clearly, appropriately matched black and ethnic minority people will generally be better able than their white peers to represent the interests of individual black and ethnic minority service users in this way. However, some citizen advocacy schemes have few, if any, black volunteers. Volunteering has

---

Ideas In Practice

Leeds Advocacy

Leeds Advocacy for people with learning difficulties is a citizen advocacy project working within an area which includes several different black and ethnic minority communities.

Recognising that, previously, services have not met the needs of black and ethnic minority people with learning difficulties, the project has prioritised the need to recruit advocates for black and ethnic minority people with learning difficulties. They now have black and ethnic minority people on the Management Committee and have appointed a black co-ordinator who works primarily, but not specifically, with Asian people with learning difficulties. One of her tasks is to assist her colleagues to understand more clearly black and ethnic minority issues in advocacy.

Contact: Juliet Prager or Pami Sahota
Joint Co-ordinators
Leeds Advocacy
c/o Potternewton Mansion
Harehills Lane
Leeds LS7 4HB

Tel: 0532 626534

Avon Citizen Advocacy

Avon Citizen Advocacy aims to support a wide range of advocates from all races and ethnic backgrounds, partnered with people living in a range of different settings, such as hospitals, hostels and homes in the community.

The project has 36 advocates and 32 partners. Of these, there are now three black advocates and two black partners. To date, the management committee is all white.

Contact: Mark Graham or Liz Hine
Avon Citizen Advocacy Office
Basement
182 St Michael's Hill
Bristol BS2 8DE

Tel: 0272 739327

tended traditionally to attract mainly (white) middle-class people, so some citizen advocacy schemes are now taking active steps to recruit black advocates (see boxes on this and the previous page).

Drives to recruit more volunteers from black and ethnic minority communities are important and should be developed and encouraged. Citizen advocacy recruitment programmes must be geared towards all sections of the community. For example, all materials should be written in relevant community languages and the images and content should reflect people's ethnic origins and culture. (Further details about recruitment can be found in Chapter 7, Black and Ethnic Minority Staff.)

Advocacy is not new to black and ethnic minority communities. In many cases, particularly in communities whose first language is not English, a small number of bilingual people (usually women) play a key role on a voluntary basis, supporting others as they deal with various authorities and organisations. These voluntary advocates have the triple duties of interpreting, providing practical support and advice, and speaking up on behalf of others, and invariably support several people at any given time. Because of their small community networks and experience of inadequate or inappropriate services, black and ethnic minority people are often highly skilled at developing and maintaining such supportive relationships.

A big challenge facing citizen advocacy schemes is to recognise, value and support the informal advocacy which already exists in black and ethnic minority communities.

CARLTON AND LENNOX

Carlton is 18 years old and of Afro-Caribbean origin. He suffered a lot of bad experiences in the past. He was beaten at school by some teachers and his mother had to take him out of the school. Once, during an organised visit, he was accidently shot by an airgun pellet and hurt. Consequently, his mother was very worried about him going out on his own, and so kept him indoors. This all changed when he met Lennox, his advocate, who is twenty years old and also Afro-Caribbean. Both young men were born in Britain and had known each other in their childhood. They had a shared history. This was a reintroduction. Lennox proved to be a wonderful companion. This relationship has become an important one in their lives. Carlton's mother's anxieties have now eased.

Black Advocate, White Partner

Black people who become advocates to white people may face difficulties, including racism. These problems must be acknowledged and the organisation must provide appropriate support.

Andrea, a young black woman, is an advocate for Jean who is white:

Andrea and Jean are both 24 years old and were carefully matched in every way. The only difference being that Andrea was black and Jean was white. This was of some concern to the Advocacy Office since Jean was known to have expressed racist views in the past and might not have accepted a black advocate. There was discussion about whether this should be discussed with her before a meeting was arranged. It was decided that they should not do this but would see how the relationship developed. The initial meeting was not too bad. However, afterwards, Jean remarked "... to be quite honest, I was surprised she was black". This statement then allowed the subject to be discussed and racist views challenged.

ADVOCACY OFFICE CO-ORDINATOR

Other Issues

Advocates who are experienced and committed may still encounter problems when faced with powerful individuals (in this case a Consultant) who may not appreciate the issues confronting black and ethnic minority people in their use of services for people with learning difficulties.

The case I allude to is one concerning an Asian family and their multiply and severely handicapped daughter. This young lady had traditionally taken short term care on an irregular, but needs basis, usually to enable the family to have respite during religious holidays or to return home to Pakistan, I believe. On the occasion in hand, through the Community Mental Handicap Team, a referral was made to the Consultant in Mental Handicap responsible for short term care to enable the family to return home for some major event in Pakistan. In normal circumstances there would have been no problem with this request, but for the length of time, which was approximately 8–10 weeks, the Consultant concerned did not feel that the care provision within the hospital was justified as the father was remaining within this country. It was, however, pointed out that it would not be "normal" within the culture of the family for the father to perform for the intimate caring needs of his daughter — this young lady is doubly incontinent, extremely frail and severely handicapped. No heed was paid of this and the Community Mental Handicap Team sought advice from a local charity which acted as an advocate for people with learning difficulties in the area.

The case was taken up with vigour and representation was made first to me, from where I outlined the situation within the NHS and the Consultant's responsibility in relation to their role as Responsible Medical Officer and their inherent right to admit or not to admit. I directed them to the local District Medical Officer, Unit General Manager responsible for Mental Handicap Services in the area, Regional Medical Officer and the relevant officers with the then DHSS.

Although extreme pressure was brought to bear on those very senior Medical Officers, the particular doctor concerned would not move. In the end, through myself and the District General Manager (who has the right to direct, in extreme circumstances, the admission of patients, which was the action we took in this particular case) the young lady was admitted.

As a result of this particular case, a complete review of short term care arrangements for the health authority concerned has taken place led by myself in conjunction with senior officers in both health authorities. We have attempted to outline the implications in relation to racial discrimination with the Consultant concerned, as indeed have the Regional Medical Officer and the District Medical Officer for the area, but to no avail. There is still stalemate in relation to moving the Consultant to more flexible admission criteria for persons with a handicap under her remit.

Assistant General Manager, Mental Handicap Services

Conflict of Interest

In any relationship there is potential for conflict. When people are from different backgrounds, a special effort may be required to avoid specific difficulties or misunderstandings which may arise from the difference. The legacy of racism is all too enduring. White advocates who choose to act on behalf of black and ethnic minority people may, nevertheless, have negative attitudes towards, and assumptions about, them. However unwitting and unconscious these long-held attitudes may be, they are still very dangerous. Citizen advocacy offices will need to be alert to such issues and act firmly to counter racist assumptions and stereotyping.

Self-Advocacy

Speaking out and standing up for one's own rights is a major challenge for people with learning difficulties. The self-advocacy movement supports and enables individuals to acquire the necessary skills. Groups of people meet to help and encourage each other to assert their interests, and to develop skills like public speaking and leading or participating in meetings. Each group has access to an adviser who is available to them as a resource.

Black and ethnic minority people are under-represented as advisers to self-advocacy groups and within the self-advocacy movement itself. Because black and ethnic minority people with learning difficulties are under-represented in further education, they have a poorer access than their white peers to self-advocacy classes within educational institutions.

Self-advocacy develops and requires some degree of self confidence and assertiveness. Sometimes art, music and movement are used to help build up people's sense of self-esteem. This needs to reflect the richness and diversity of art forms in multiracial communities.

Black and ethnic minority people with learning difficulties face a double challenge of a handicap and racism, but the dimension of race is rarely addressed in confidence building and assertiveness training.

For information on self-advocacy generally:

Contact: People First
          Oxford House
          Derbyshire Street
          London E2 6HG
          Tel: 071 739 3890

Or: Jackie Downer
     Lambeth Accord
     336 Brixton Road
     London SW9 7AA
     Tel: 081 274 2299 ext 130

IDEAS IN PRACTICE

Sharing Experiences: A Conference where Black People with Learning Difficulties Could Speak Out for Themselves

A group of black and white people involved in the training of staff caring for people with learning difficulties were particularly concerned about the kind of services being provided for black people and their families. They wanted to invite black people with learning difficulties and their families to come to a conference to talk about the problems they had in using day centres, hostels, group homes, hospitals and health centres.

Information was circulated in advance about the conference, which was designed to address participants' potential concerns:

Some people with learning difficulties coming to the meeting may need help from a friend so that they can join in with the meeting more easily or to make their views known to everyone else. We would welcome such friends and, although we would prefer the friend you bring to be a black friend, we would also welcome white friends. If anyone has difficulties with people understanding what they say, or if someone cannot speak English very well, please contact one of the people listed at the end of this sheet.

We would like to hear what you feel is good about the services. We feel that it is very important for us to find out what black people think about services

before we can make plans for the training of care staff. We are going to hold another meeting later on for care staff and people who plan services. We will then write a report about these meetings and give a copy to each person who came to the meeting.

We know that some black people may be worried about coming to a meeting like this and we would be happy to talk about this with anyone who wishes to telephone or write to us.

We hope that you can come to the meeting because it will be a chance for black people to say what they feel about the services for people with learning difficulties and it may help people responsible for these services to think of changes and make the services better for everyone.

Contact: Peter Richies
London Based Training
            Consortium
(Training for Care)
9 Tavistock Place
London WC1H 9SN

Tel: 071 388 2041

For a report of the conference, see Baxter (1990b). (See also Chapter 8, page 205.)

Black Self-Advocacy Groups in Hackney and Brixton

The Sharing Experiences conference was successful in developing black advocacy groups. People who attended have been meeting since. One group has been established in Hackney where about twelve self-advocates meet every few weeks. Another group is planned for Brixton.

Contact: Peter Ferns
4 Grosvenor Road
Luton
Beds LU3 2EG

Tel: 0582 594579

CHALLENGING BEHAVIOUR

A very small number of people with learning difficulties at times exhibit behaviour which is so challenging that services have extreme difficulty meeting their needs.

Challenging behaviours may be apparently unpredictable. They may occur sporadically or very frequently. They may be particularly violent or distressing. The behaviours may involve aggression to others, self-injury, destruction of the environment or other distressing or life-threatening features which necessitate special provision. The person may be very difficult for relatives or staff to understand and have sympathy for. He or she may be very difficult to control when the challenging behaviour occurs. This may be associated with psychiatric disturbance but may equally be associated with poor or inappropriate communication or with disturbance of social relationships (Blunden and Allen, 1987). Hence, most of the challenging behaviour appears to serve as a method of communication — to avoid demands, contacts or people being near.

People who are recognised as having challenging behaviour may have a history of long term deprivation, neglect and frequent moves in and out of institutions. Services commonly respond by excluding them from activities which they could otherwise enjoy. Their movements may be restricted and high doses of medication may be prescribed.

CAROL'S STORY

The following story was told to us by a residential social worker. She felt that Carol's experiences epitomise what living in a white society can do to a black person with learning difficulties.

Carol is a 28 year old Afro-Caribbean woman who is dyslexic and whose learning difficulty is mild. When she reached puberty she developed a personality disorder which resulted in her being taken into care at the age of 14. Since then she has been in and out of institutions.

Carol, however, lived independently for some time. During one of her spells in care she met her boyfriend who lived in a nearby hostel for people with learning difficulties. She became pregnant by him and was very pleased about the prospect of having a baby. Her boyfriend was, however, moved and she was apparently forced to have the pregnancy terminated against her will. She was obviously deeply distressed by this and became very disturbed by the loss. She talked a lot about "the baby which was taken away from me because it was handicapped" and of having "seen it in a coffin". Her subsequent behaviour has become increasingly disturbed. She seems desperate for a close relationship with people, including men. She is obviously, however, distrustful and fearful of losing them. When people get close to her she, therefore, behaves in a very hostile and dismissive manner — alternating between need and rejection.

Carol began to be aggressive and to hit people, as a result of which she spent a year in a large hospital. She was later discharged into hostel care in core and cluster accommodation set in a traditional white middle class area living in a flat among elderly people. Attempts to get residents to relate to her positively failed. She was feared and most residents openly expressed, in very racist terms, their resentment of her living there. She was desperately isolated. Nevertheless, her hostel placement lasted for about a year.

Carol's ability to cope with her environment declined sharply when there were significant staff changes. She did not hurt people, but aimed her frustration at furniture. She was placed under increasing control, with 24 hour supervision and a bus escort. She rebelled and recently expressed her anger by hitting a member of staff who is now claiming criminal injuries, believing this to be consistent with normalisation. She has refused to work with "the black bastard", Carol, under any circumstances, despite the offer of additional support and safeguards. She has also encouraged two other workers to do the same.

To date, the police have brought no charges, but it is likely that if a similar incident occurs, Carol will be admitted to a psychiatric hospital. Three members of staff are determined not to let this happen because they know it need not. They have started to work the extra shift needed to keep Carol living independently and are also training and sensitising other staff to share this work with them. They say: "We have to duck sometimes, but we have a certain confidence that nothing will happen. Those staff who refuse to work with Carol are shift workers, working only 20 hours per week. They do not see this work as a career and are not interested. You can't expect such people to take these kind of risks. It is up to those of us who care to do it."

Additional Difficulties

Black and ethnic minority people may have additional difficulties which contribute to their behaviour being labelled as "challenging".

➤ **Communication difficulties** — It has been recognised that challenging behaviour reflects problems of communication. The person concerned has some difficulty in expressing their wishes in the usually accepted way, and the carer or service provider has difficulty in listening to and recognising their needs. For a variety of reasons, black and ethnic minority people are less likely to be heard, understood and have their needs and wishes responded to by (white) service providers. These problems will be compounded by language difficulties where they exist, particularly since people who speak little English are often treated with hostility and intolerance rather than sympathy or empathy.

➤ **Cultural differences** — These may result in behaviour being mistakenly labelled as "challenging". Tone of voice and non-verbal signals are all part and parcel of communication and mutual understanding. Eye contact or lack of it, head and body movements, facial expressions, gesticulations, touching and personal space (i.e. physical distance from others) are all learnt during our upbringing. Difficulties can be exacerbated if these finer points of communication are interpreted inappropriately.

Misunderstanding arose particularly where food was not eaten because it was not what people were used to. This could be seen as challenging. Gesticulations could be seen as a behaviour problem.

Black Social Worker, Sharing Experiences Conference

➤ **Racial harassment** — The stigma of being black as well as having learning difficulties can raise additional problems for families. A father of an 18 year old boy with epilepsy who lives on a council estate in a predominantly white working class area told us:

Safder is very active. He gets frustrated if he is locked up inside all day. He will sometimes get violent if he feels locked in. We are so afraid of letting him out because he gets a lot of verbal abuse from other people on the streets — not only because of his handicap but about his colour. This makes him very frustrated and a fight could start. I applied to the housing department for an extension — like a big playroom in my back garden. I do not mind not having a garden as long as my son can walk freely without being called names and poked at. All the council can come up with is excuses about why they cannot give me a grant. If they knew how we all suffer, I am sure they would help — but they don't understand. Maybe they can't or they don't want to.

Ali Shah's Story

Ali Shah's story illustrates how many service practices work against black and ethnic minority people with learning difficulties with challenging behaviour.

Ali Shah is a Muslim young man. He is one of six children. His father often works away from home and his mother finds it difficult to look after him amidst all her other responsibilities. He is the only black resident in a home in which all the staff are white, although there is an Asian social worker attached to Ali's case. Ali goes to his family home for the weekends.

Recently, Ali has begun to show severe challenging behaviour. He has stopped communicating by speech, so that it is difficult for staff at the residential home to understand his needs. Ali's mother speaks Urdu and a little English. It has, therefore, been difficult to establish a meaningful relationship between staff and family. Ali's increasing challenging behaviour has worsened an already strained relationship. The staff believe that this recent behaviour is closely linked to his family life, and are frustrated because they feel Ali's family has not helped them identify the cause of his deteriorating behaviour. As a result of our interest in this area of work we were asked to talk to Ali's mother to see if we would help to find out what the problems were.

We found that Ali's family were also greatly distressed about the situation and feared that Ali's behaviour would result in his admission to a hospital ward. At home he continues to speak a mixture of Urdu and English. He appears to enjoy being at home where there are people who can understand him and he can participate in family activities. We discovered that Ali had suffered a series of losses over the years, due to rapid turnover of staff and residents. He is aware that, on leaving school, he will be moving soon to another residential home. This fractured life has resulted in him being insecure and distrustful.

Because of her feelings of guilt and love, Ali's mother "overcompensates" by indulging Ali in a lot of Indian videos, which he greatly enjoys. Her approach to Ali is one of the main sources of friction between family and staff.

A psychologist was called in to develop a programme for changing Ali's challenging behaviour. A "solution" of reward and punishment was identified, but this conflicted with his mother's approach. Progress was slow and this led the psychologist to suspect that Ali had a mental illness — manic depression. The psychologists involved could not agree on this diagnosis. The family were not really consulted.

Recently, Ali's behaviour showed some improvement. This has coincided with the arrival of Clinton — a new friend whom he enjoys being with. Clinton (who also has "challenging behaviour") is Afro-Caribbean. It was felt by some of the staff that Ali's improvement in behaviour was because he was no longer the only black person in the home.

Since the involvement of the psychologists, Mrs Shah's original fear has increased, that Ali may be taken from her and locked away in a hospital. When we last spoke to her, she was still desperately frightened and confused. Her main plea for help was that we should find her a doctor who spoke her language, who could then explain to her Ali's learning difficulties and the current situation.

Stereotyping and Labelling

The term "challenging behaviour" is derived from the perspective of the care providers. It attempts to shift the blame from the person with learning difficulties and emphasises the responsibility of services to respond to and meet appropriately the needs of such individuals.

In Britain, black and ethnic minority people are often viewed stereotypically as a threat. Their experiences of the criminal justice system and mental health services indicate that they are often treated as a menace (Baxter, 1990b). Black people generally stand a higher risk of being diagnosed as having a challenging mental illness. A large proportion are misdiagnosed, their normal signs of distress being misinterpreted as mental illness (Littlewood and Lipsedge, 1982). Police are more likely to be involved in the enforcement of the mental health laws with black people than with white people. Because of the image of black people (particularly Afro-Caribbeans) as being violent and aggressive, they are more likely to be detained in high security units (NACRO, 1986).

Black people are still often viewed with a great deal of suspicion and as being a danger to people and property.

At the Sharing Experiences Conference a young black woman with learning difficulties who watched her friend having an epileptic fit said to us:

I have seen a fit before … Sometimes it happens on the streets. When this happens the police come and they can't do anything, they just think that the person is angry.

Within services for people with learning difficulties these views and images result in black and ethnic minority people being labelled as posing a challenge to the service system.

I am very concerned about the numbers of young Afro-Caribbean men who are being referred to me. Often they come to the attention of the department via the police. Most of them are products of the 1960s and 70s when many Afro-Caribbeans were put in ESN schools. They have now reached school leaving age and have to face the wider society with no skills at all. They fall prey to the police who are ready to assume that they are a danger to others. They are provoked and often arrested and then handed back to me to sort out.

BLACK CONSULTANT PSYCHIATRIST

In our group home if one Asian person does something wrong or upsets the others then all the other Asian residents and the rest of the Asian community gets the blame. They are all then labelled as challenging and the staff never let them live it down. It is really frightening to see how much power they have to make or break a person's life.

AFRO-CARIBBEAN MENTAL HANDICAP COMMUNITY NURSE

JOHN ABBOT'S STORY

John is 22 years old. He is extremely active and needs 24 hours supervision on an individual basis. His parents who are in their early sixties have often had to return to Jamaica for family reasons. John was in a large institution for some time. He eventually returned to live with his parents, but they can no longer have him at home because of their failing health. At the age of 20 he went to live in a home and responded well to individualised care. Unfortunately, this arrangement proved too expensive for the Social Services Department and John returned to his parents. Later, John's father had to go back to Jamaica to look after his own elderly parents and asked the Social Services Department to take over his care.

John now lives in a large home with one-to-one staff support, but the home is awaiting closure and he is the only person waiting to be rehoused. Both parents originally wanted to return to Jamaica and take John with them. With the considerable help of a committed social worker they explored the situation of services there. Their final decision was to let him stay in England. They and the Social Services Department have started to think of finding a home for him in the community.

John's parents have suggested that he takes over the tenancy of their house (when they return to Jamaica) and that the Social Services put staff in to look after him. This could cost as much as £70,000 per year. This solution was, however, rejected by the Social Services as too expensive, although the estimated average cost of caring for a person with challenging behaviour is often between £30,000 and £100,000 per year. One social worker suggested that perhaps the idea was too simple.

Young black men tend to be labelled due to these stereotypes. Reports are written in a racist way — having these stereotypes means that they get no real help at the early signs of showing distress since the services either tend to underreact or overreact.

SOCIAL WORKER

There are 800 residents in this hospital. But all the black men live on ward 19, the notorious "bad boys' wing". It is a new unit but was left to run down very quickly. The ward is seen as a punishment for both staff and patients. It was like working with chimps in a zoo reinforced by a cage. There is a large compound with iron climbing frames and tyres.

EX-NURSE TUTOR

Working with People with Challenging Behaviour

It is important to try to understand the reasons for a person's challenging behaviour and to get a feel of their situation from their perspective. Communication difficulties and racist stereotyping and labelling, however, put black and ethnic minority people with learning difficulties at a disadvantage. They may be denied a systematic and constructive approach and the resources necessary to help "improve" their behaviour. They are more likely to be treated from a "pathological" perspective, as though there were something inherently wrong with them. As a white social worker said to us:

Staff are more ready to refuse to work with clients who are black. They make more allowances for white clients.

The implications for working from an antiracist and multicultural perspective are clear. Service providers must be aware of the prevalence of stereotypes. It is vital to confront racist ideas and prejudices, which may cause black and ethnic minority people with learning difficulties to be labelled as challenging, and which prevent them from receiving appropriate assistance and services.

Approaches need to be flexible and creative to meet the needs of individuals. Where management and professional support for workers is good, it will be easier for resources to be reallocated to programmes for black and ethnic minority people with challenging behaviour.

Ideas In Practice

Information Exchange

The King's Fund Centre runs an information exchange which provides support for those groups and individuals actually involved in planning and setting up community services for people with challenging behaviour. The initiative provides a forum for people to exchange views and experiences. Through the exchange, they hope to:

➤ produce an informal "register" of summaries of schemes and projects for people with an interest in community services for those with challenging behaviour

➤ produce a newsletter giving information on current developments in services and plans

➤ organise conferences at which planners, practitioners and carers can meet and exchange information

➤ produce a follow-up publication to *Facing the Challenge* (Blunden and Allen, 1987) based on the actual experiences of people attempting to put these ideas into practice

People interested in participating in any of these initiatives are encouraged to contact:

Joan Rush
King's Fund Centre
126 Albert Street
London NW1 7NF

Tel: 071 267 6111

Training

The Workers Educational Association (WEA), Western District, has incorporated the element of race into a new training programme for staff and others aimed at developing skills and strategies in relation to challenging behaviour. As part of the course, a local black parent who has a child with learning difficulties came and shared her experiences with course participants.

Contact: Mandy Neville, Tutor Organiser
Workers Educational Association
40 Morse Road
Redfield
Bristol BS5 9LB

Tel: 0272 351764/351765

REFERENCES

Baxter C (1990a): *Sharing Experiences to Challenge Practice. A Report of Two Workshops Around Services for Black People with Learning Difficulties.* London, CCETSW. Forthcoming.

Baxter C (1990b): "Parallels between the social role perception of people with learning difficulties and black and ethnic minority people". In: Brechin A and Walmsley J (eds): *Making Connections.* Milton Keynes, Hodder and Stoughton, in association with the Open University Press.

Blunden R and Allen D (eds) (1987): *Facing the Challenge. An Ordinary Life for People with Learning Difficulties and Challenging Behaviour.* London, King's Fund Centre.

Brailey M, Daghilian S and Taylor M (1989): *Meeting Special Needs in the Community.* Glasgow, Integrate.

Brown C (1984): *Black and White Britain. Third PSI Survey.* London, Heinemann.

Brown C (1990): "Racial inequality in the British labour market". *Employment Institute Economic Report,* June, Vol 5, No 4.

Brown C and Jay P (1985): *Racial Discrimination: Seventeen Years After the Act.* London, PSI.

Bryan B, Dadzie S and Scafe S (1985): *The Heart of the Race. Black Women's Lives in Britain.* London, Virago.

Cocking I and Athwal S (1990): "A special case for special treatment". *Social Work Today,* 8 February, pp 12–13.

Compton A Y (1989): "Multiracial perspectives on sex education". *Sexual and Marital Therapy,* Vol 4, No 1, pp 75–85.

Craft A (1987): *Mental Handicap and Sexuality.* Tunbridge Wells, Costello.

Craft A and Craft M (1979): *Handicapped Married Couples.* London, Routledge and Kegan Paul.

Cranny K (1988): *The Lack of Provision for People with Special Housing Needs within the Black Community in Glasgow.* Glasgow, Glasgow Special Housing Group.

Harper G (1989): "Life sharing". *Community Living,* April, pp 6–7.

Huhne C (1989): "Ethnic minorities have double the white unemployment rate". *Guardian,* March 10.

Janner M (1988–89): "Mr Cohen and Mr Joseph". *CMH Newsletter,* Winter, No 55, pp 2–3.

King's Fund Centre (1984): *An Ordinary Working Life*. London, King's Fund Centre.

King's Fund Centre (1988): *Ties and Connections: An Ordinary Community Life for People with Learning Difficulties*. London, King's Fund Centre.

Littlewood R and Lipsedge M (1982): *Aliens and Alienists: Ethnic Minorities and Psychiatry*. Harmondsworth, Penguin.

Marshall M and Porter D (1990): *Read Easy*. London, J. Whitaker and Sons.

Mattinson J (1975): *Marriage and Mental Handicap*. London, Tavistock Institute.

NACRO (1986): *Black People and the Criminal Justice System. Summary of the Report of the NACRO Race Issues Advisory Committee*. London, NACRO.

NIACE (1987): *Equal Opportunities Policy*. Leicester, NIACE.

Nottingham Social Services Department (1987): *Sample Study of Black Families with a Mentally Handicapped Member*. Nottingham, Nottingham Social Services Department. Unpublished.

Nzira V (1989): "Race: The ingredients of good practice". In Philpot T (ed): *The Residential Opportunity? The Wagner Report and After*. Wallington, Reed Business Publishing/Community Care.

Residential Care. A Positive Choice (The Wagner Report) (1988). London, NISW/HMSO.

Richardson A and Ritchie J (1989): *Developing Friendships. Enabling People with Learning Difficulties to Make and Maintain Friends*. London, PSI.

SSI (Social Services Inspectorate) (1989): *Inspection of Day Services for People with Mental Handicap*. London, Department of Health.

Sutcliffe J (1990): *Adults with Learning Difficulties: Education for Choice and Empowerment*. Buckingham, NIACE/Open University Press.

Wiltshire P (1985): *Living and Winning*. London, Centreprise.

FURTHER READING

Residential Services For Black and Ethnic Minority People

Brown B (1989): "Race: Needed — Policy and practice". In Philpot T (ed): *The Residential Opportunity? The Wagner Report and After.* Wallington, Reed Business Publishing/Community Care.

Nzira V, Phillipson J and Sugden M (1989): "Race: A faltering first step". In Philpot T (ed): as above.

RESOURCES

Baxter, C (1987): *Hair Care of African, Afro-Caribbean and Asian Hair Types.* Cambridge, National Extension College for Training in Health and Race.

Commission for Racial Equality (CRE) (1976): *Afro Hair and Skin Care and Recipes.* London, Commission for Racial Equality.

USEFUL ADDRESSES

Federation of Black Housing Associations
374 Grays Inn Road
London WC1
Tel: 071 837 8288

Aron Mirza
Equal Opportunities Department
National Federation of Housing Associations
175 Grays Inn Road
London WC1X 8UP
Tel: 071 278 6571

Growing Older

They are not only in double jeopardy by reason of age and discrimination as has often been stated, but in triple jeopardy, at risk because they are old, because of the physical conditions and hostility under which they have to live and because services are not accessible to them.

(Norman, 1985)

Introduction

This chapter considers specific issues which need to be considered in anticipation of the increasing number of older people with learning difficulties from black and ethnic minority communities. Issues are discussed in terms of their implications both for ageing relatives or carers and for people with learning difficulties who may be bereaved.

➢ Ageing
➢ Bereavement

Ageing

In the past, most people with learning difficulties did not survive into "old age". However, the general trend in longevity is now also reflected in this section of the population.

Black and ethnic minority communities are still considered to be a young population. Traditionally, many statutory bodies have failed to recognise the existence of minority elderly people in these communities. For example, when members of the local Community Association asked Lambeth Council for their policy on Afro-Caribbean senior citizens, they were informed that there were no files on this group of people as they did not exist (Sevedin and Gorosch-Tomlinson, 1984).

Although it is generally true (with the exception of some Italian, Polish and other Eastern European communities) that the black and ethnic minority population in this country is still relatively young, the situation is changing. The 1971 Census indicated that there were 26,400 people of pensionable age born in the New Commonwealth and Pakistan living in Britain. By 1981 the estimated figure was 87,117. The ageing black population has increasing implications for future services. As the size of this section of the community grows, there has to be a growing awareness of their needs.

Owing to economic and social circumstances, the extended family system in black communities is not always able or available to care for its elders. However, existing sheltered accommodation does not cater for their needs because of different cultural, linguistic, religious and social norms. There are clear indications of a preference by black and ethnic minority communities for facilities and schemes which reflect their aspirations and lifestyles (SCEMSC, 1986; Glendenning and Pearson, 1987).

The needs of black and ethnic minority elders are beginning to be addressed within some voluntary and statutory services aimed at the general population, but services specifically for black and ethnic minority elders have also developed, often to fill the gaps left by inappropriate statutory provision (Glendenning and Pearson, 1987).

➤ Some meals on wheels services now offer a wider choice of foods.

➤ Home care workers from black and ethnic minority communities have been actively recruited in some areas.

➤ There are housing developments which have been designed particularly to meet the needs of black and ethnic minority people.

The following issues need to be specifically considered for black and ethnic minority elderly people with learning difficulties.

Patterns of Retirement

Black and ethnic minority communities in Britain are generally established and settled. There are those, however, who may wish to return to their countries of origin in later life (Fenton, 1987). Situations may arise in which younger family members may want their older relative with learning difficulties to return "home" for their retirement. Ageing parents may also wish to take their sons or daughters with learning difficulties home with them. (See, for example, John Abbott's story, page 152.)

Other parents, as they grow older, may become too frail to continue to carry the responsibility of their relatives with learning difficulties, but still wish for them to be cared for in the family home. Families facing such difficult decisions will need practical guidance and sensitive support from service providers about the options available.

Most elderly people will want meaningful occupation in their retirement. People with learning difficulties are no exception, though they may need extra support and assistance to enable them to achieve this. For many black and ethnic minority elderly people it is the opportunity to be involved in the lives of younger members of the family that they most look forward to in retirement (Fenton, 1987). This is particularly true in extended family households. In the majority culture, the nuclear family is the norm. Thus (white) service providers and (black) families may have different ideas about how best to help black and ethnic minority people with learning difficulties to achieve a fulfilling retirement.

Reminiscing is an important part of elderly people's daily lives. This can only happen where the people with whom they interact share common experiences and language. Placing them in elderly people's homes where most residents and staff do not share their culture, life experiences or language will increase their isolation and loneliness.

Specific Services

The mainstream services provided for elderly people may not always be appropriate for black and ethnic minority people. Meals on Wheels for example will need to reflect the dietary preferences of black and ethnic minority people, as will day services and lunch clubs for elderly people. Similarly, home care workers will need to demonstrate an awareness of and sensitivity to people's culture and lifestyle. Residential homes, too, must cater for the needs of black and ethnic minority elderly people. (See Chapter 5, Adulthood, for a fuller discussion of residential services; and Glendenning and Pearson (1987) for a fuller discussion of service initiatives for black and ethnic minority elders.)

IDEAS IN PRACTICE

The following are examples of some schemes developed by black and ethnic minority communities to help meet the needs of elderly people (including those with mental and physical disabilities) in their locality.

Moss Side Afro-Caribbean Care Group

The Moss Side Afro-Caribbean Care Group for the Elderly and Infirm provides a meeting place for Afro-Caribbean elderly people. There are several members with physical and mental disabilities. The Group meets Tuesdays and Thursdays and aims to:

➤ help elderly people gain confidence and encourage self-help

➤ raise the profile of black elderly people in this community and draw in the isolated and unattached

The Care Group also has a visiting team to visit the sick and house-bound and members are encouraged to visit each other.

The Group has the use of a minibus to get people to and from the Centre and for day trips and outings. There is also a luncheon club which provides a mixture of Afro-Caribbean and English food.

The project is funded by Manchester Social Services Department with assistance from the Council for Voluntary Services and Manchester Age Concern.

Contact: Raphael Phipps
           Birley Community
               Education Centre
           Chichester Road
           Hulme
           Manchester 15
           Tel: 061 226 1416

The Asians' Sheltered Residential Accommodation (ASRA)

ASRA started a pioneering venture by providing sheltered accommodation for Asian elderly people in Leicester. They began by converting derelict property, but they are now developing purpose-built property. ASRA started out of concern by a group of Asians for their elderly. They are helping those who do not want to live in high rise blocks or on outlying estates away from the Asian community or who are living in overcrowded family situations. The service is expanding and there are similar developments in London, Coventry, Nottingham and Loughborough.

Contact: Asian Sheltered Housing
           Association (ASRA)
           34 Princess Road West
           Leicester LE1 6TJ
           Tel: 0533 558121

ASRA Asian Housing Association

This is another Asian housing association with the same name, which also provides housing for elderly Asian people with special needs.

Contact: Bala Thakrar
ASRA
155 Kennington Park Road
London SE11 4JJ

Mission Dine Club

A luncheon club for black and ethnic minority elderly people which meets at Willesden Sports Centre in London. Particular interest is paid to the needs of disabled people.

Contact: Betty Asafu Adjaye
78 Clark Court
Stilton Crescent
London NW10 8DJ

Tel: 081 961 5843

The Standing Conference of Ethnic Minority Senior Citizens (SCEMSC)

SCEMSC is an umbrella organisation working for the improvement of day services and community care for elderly people from black and ethnic minority communities. Specific aims are to:

➢ bring together information about services and other provisions for ethnic minority elderly

➢ act as a resource and reference centre for statutory and voluntary agencies seeking advice

➢ instigate research and provide a directory of relevant services for ethnic minority elderly

➢ organise conferences and meetings and provide other resources to further its work

A joint project between SCEMSC and the National Institute for the Deaf was set up in May 1990. The aim is to develop training and training materials for community workers on the care of deaf elderly people from ethnic minority communities. Community workers from ten different ethnic communities will be trained in their own language with a view to cascading of training amongst service users themselves.

Contact: Dr Manchego
Acting Director
SCEMSC
5–5a Westminster Bridge Road
London SE1 7XW

Tel: 071 928 0095

Bereavement

Ways of marking death have varied throughout history and according to current customs and religions. In Britain in the latter half of the twentieth century there has been a decline in the ceremony and formal display of mourning which was common in the nineteenth century. The decline has been variously explained as caused by a weakening in established religious influence, by people living much longer, by fewer people dying at home so that death has come to be regarded as a problem for the welfare state.

(Oswin, 1981)

Death and bereavement are distressing events for everyone. Today, death is a taboo subject in majority British culture. It is not readily discussed. Dying and bereavement are often viewed as a personal, private affair involving only close family and friends. The bereaved are not expected to openly express their feelings and their grief.

These expectations and norms, however, may not be the same for all communities in multiracial Britain. There may be marked differences in how people cope with loss and the strategies that help them do so. All people, including those with learning difficulties, are individuals and will grieve in their own way. Some people may rely on the therapeutic value of the expression of strong emotions to help them come to terms with their loss. They may also rely on the "supportive grieving" of others concerned.

Strong religious faith may mean that, despite the feelings of loss, some people may be better able to come to terms with the death of a family member. They may find solace in their belief that "the Lord giveth and the Lord taketh away" or "it is the will of Allah".

Death of a Parent

It is common for children and for people with learning difficulties to be protected from upsetting situations. It is also a commonly held view that people with learning difficulties do not have the same emotional needs as others. Their grief is often not acknowledged, and their need for support through death and bereavement may go unmet. For those who are not able to verbalise or easily express their feelings, there may be a particular danger that their feelings are ignored or misinterpreted.

People with learning difficulties may need other kinds of help when bereaved. The death of a parent may result in them moving house or even neighbourhood, involving the further loss of familiar surroundings,

---

MARIA'S STORY

I was unaccustomed to these surroundings and sat awkwardly on the hard church pew. Next to me, Maria softly sang the chants of her faith, her face lit by the candle in her hand. Noticing my stare, she patted my arm reassuringly and gave back a smile that wrinkled her whole face.

Maria had been born a Greek in Cyprus, and church had always played an important part in her own life and culture. When she was still a child her parents had brought her to England with her sister. They had settled in North London. As far as I know she hadn't gone to school but had spent her days either with her mum at home or accompanying her father to the church. She still remembers helping her father make candles for the church.

Six years ago her father died. Maria was devastated, but by taking part in the intricacies of the funeral — by all accounts an elaborate affair involving the entire local Greek Cypriot community — she found a way to say goodbye.

Less than two years later her mother was to join her husband after a long time in hospital. Maria was left alone. This time "the services" decided it was not appropriate for her to attend the funeral, and she never found out where her mother had gone.

The sister and her family were embarrassed about her and anyway, they said, they had a business and a family to manage. Thus Maria's life was soon in the control of the services. Her home was called a "project" and was occupied by two teenagers sent in to care for her. They did not belong to her culture, and she did not understand …

In this way, Maria's life was barren of everything she knew, even down to the food she was accustomed to eat; her music, her self-expression, dignity, and the respect due to a woman of her age in her culture …

Maria's life is a little better now. Two outreach workers from her own Greek culture take her twice a week to a day centre for Greek Cypriot people. The young people who now live in her flat are supported, trained and monitored, and there are closer links with the church. She has even been helped to go on holiday to the place of her birth.

(FROM STEELE, 1989)

---

possessions, friends and neighbours. For many people with learning difficulties, especially those from black and ethnic minority communities, this move could be the first time they have been away from family and community. It may also involve a far greater professional involvement in their lives. Even where there are appropriate local facilities to move to, some families may be reluctant to let their relative go. There may be strong family ties, a feeling of responsibility as well as personal experience of racism and alienation in society. These factors will exacerbate the usual fear of seeing one's relatives go to live in a strange environment with different people.

Sharing

It is essential that there is continuity in the bereaved person's life at this time. Established routines, norms and experiences should not suddenly cease. This can only be ensured by obtaining detailed information about the bereaved person's life. Where the person with learning difficulties is from a black or ethnic minority community, difficulties in communication between professionals and relatives could entail that loss of important details. There is also a risk that professionals will not appreciate the significance of a particular activity or possession in the bereaved person's life.

Reacting

Differences in reactions and expectations after the death of a loved one are to be expected. In some situations a restrained approach may appear uncaring and unsupportive, whereas a more openly emotional response would be more fitting. The language used, the interpretation of what has happened, the understanding of what death is, and the rituals of grieving will vary between communities and between individuals. Different views and responses should be respected and recognised as important in making sense of loss.

Some families may expect the person with learning difficulties to attend the funeral and to look at their deceased relative. Even if this is not what white service providers are used to, it may be helpful to seek advice from others in the community — church members or people from the mosque or gurdwara will be able to advise.

Practical Support

Family beliefs and traditions regarding death and bereavement should be maintained and secular and religious beliefs respected. Practical means of support may include providing familiar meals and other such things in the immediate surroundings to ensure that the person has opportunities to visit the grave or to engage in other activities to mark their mourning.

The formal procedures which have to be followed after a death can be very upsetting. Coping with this will be even more traumatic if people do not understand the system. Some relatives may need explanations about what is required and practical assistance, for example, in registering the death and contacting funeral directors, or with transferring the body abroad.

Families will need particular help and support if a postmortem is required. This may conflict with some people's religious beliefs and ways will have to be sought to minimise the distress.

REFERENCES

Fenton S (1987): *Ageing Minorities: Black People as They Grow Old in Britain.* London, Commission for Racial Equality.

Glendenning F and Pearson M (1987): *The Health Needs of Black and Ethnic Minority Elders.* Working Papers on the Health of Older People, No 6. Keele, Health Education Authority, in association with the Centre for Social Gerontology, University of Keele.

Norman A (1985): *Triple Jeopardy: Growing Old in a Second Homeland.* London, Centre for Policy on Ageing.

Oswin M (1981): *Bereavement and Mentally Handicapped People.* London, King's Fund Centre.

Sevedin A M and Gorosch-Tomlinson D (1984): "They Said We Didn't Exist". *Social Work Today,* 2 April, pp 14–15.

Standing Conference of Ethnic Minority Senior Citizens (SCEMSC) (1986): *Ethnic Minority Senior Citizens: The Question of Policy.* London, SCEMSC.

Steel D (1989): "Thinking about culture". *CMH Newsletter,* Spring, No 56, p 6.

FURTHER READING

Hogg J, Moss S and Cooke D (1988): "Ageing and mental handicap". In Leighton A (ed): *Mental Handicap in the Community*. Cambridge, Woodhead-Faulkner.

Standing Conference of Ethnic Minority Senior Citizens (SCEMSC) (1987): *Making a Reality of Residential Care for Ethnic Minority Elderly — A report*. London, SCEMSC. Available from SCEMSC, cost £5.60.

Age Concern (1974): *Elderly Ethnic Minorities*. London, Age Concern.

Glendenning F (ed) (1979): *The Elders in Ethnic Minorities*. Stoke on Trent, Beth Johnson Foundation, in association with the Department of Adult Education, Keele University and the Commission for Racial Equality.

Association of Directors of Social Services (1983): *Social Services and Ethnic Minorities: Report of a Questionnaire Survey on Social Services Departments and Ethnic Minorities*. Taunton, DSS.

Commission for Racial Equality (CRE) (1981): *A Guide to Services for Ethnic Elderly*. London, CRE.

RESOURCES

Leaflets

The Right to Grieve. A leaflet for helping people with learning difficulties who are bereaved. March 1981. Available from Joan Rush, King's Fund Centre, 126 Albert Street, London NW1 7NF. Tel: 071 267 6111.

Audio Visual Material

An Introduction to Buddhism and *An Introduction to Hinduism* contain audio cassettes, a study guide and reading material. Open University (1984). Available from the Learning Materials Service, PO Box 188, Milton Keynes.

Grief is a film which talks about different cultural reactions to grief and includes a sequence on a Vietnamese soldier being returned to his village for cremation. Good for starting a discussion. It is distributed by Concord Films, 201 Felixstowe Road, Ipswich, Suffolk IP3 9BJ. Tel: 0473 76012.

Organisations

Federation of Black Housing Associations
374 Grays Inn Road
London WC1

Tel: 071 837 8288

Lorreene Hunte Foundation for Black Bereaved Families
11 Kingston Square
London SE19 1JE

Tel: 081 761 7228

Standing Committee for Ethnic Minority Senior Citizens
5–5a Westminster Bridge Road
London WC1

Tel: 071 928 0095

Black and Ethnic Minority Staff

We don't come as surrogate white people but with a set of experiences which are fundamentally different to those which have traditionally made up the white liberal profession of social work.

Josie Durrant, talking at Focus Consultancy Conference, October 30, 1989 (Community Care, November 9, 1989, p 4)

Introduction

To meet the needs of black and ethnic communities effectively, staff with the appropriate background must be employed and appropriate training given. This chapter examines the position of black and ethnic minority staff within health, community and social welfare services.

➤ Recruitment
➤ Marginalisation of Black and Ethnic Minority Staff
➤ Specialist Staff
➤ Support for Black and Ethnic Minority Staff

Staff development and training are discussed in Chapter 8, Working Towards Antiracist Services.

Recruitment

There are no national figures which show the numbers and positions of black and ethnic minority people working in social and welfare services, but local studies have shown that black people are on the whole under-represented (Doyal et al, 1980; Torkington, 1983; CRE, 1983b). Where they are employed, whatever the professions and staff grades, black and ethnic minority people tend to occupy lower positions, being over-represented in low status work and specialities, and under-represented in high status and managerial roles (Pearson, 1985).

Black social workers are scarce in most social work departments, and where they are employed, they tend to be located in the lower echelons of the labour hierarchy.

(Dominelli, 1989)

The Commission for Racial Equality found that black trainee nurses were under-represented in the 22 Schools of Nursing participating in their study (CRE, 1987). A recent report by the North East Thames Regional Health Authority's Equal Opportunities Implementation Group showed that there were no black people in senior management positions in the region. It was further noted that there

is a preponderance of white males in middle and senior management positions.

(Health Service Journal, June 1, 1989)

Previous studies have shown that black and ethnic minority doctors on the whole find it more difficult to be promoted within the health service. They are over-represented in lower medical grades, such as registrar, senior house officer and under-represented in the higher grades such as senior registrar and consultant (CRE, 1983b; Mares et al, 1985).

What underpins this appalling maldistribution of black people and ethnic minorities in health and welfare posts? One excuse often given is that services have difficulty in recruiting black staff. However, closer scrutiny of employment practices reveals policies, procedures and individual attitudes which can by their very nature exclude many black and ethnic minority people. But the suggestion that there is racial discrimination in the health and welfare services is often met with surprise and indignation. People in the caring services, proud of their commitment to others, often find it incredible that there could be even a hint of discrimination in employment practices (and service delivery) which are enshrined in policy statements, and applied uniformly to all applicants and employees.

THE 1976 RACE RELATIONS ACT: DEFINITIONS OF DISCRIMINATION

Racial discrimination, or segregation on grounds of colour, race, nationality (including citizenship) or national origin is unlawful under the Act. Discrimination in employment, training, education, the provision of goods, facilities and services, and in the disposal and management of premises can lead to prosecution. People have the right of direct access to industrial tribunals for employment cases, and to civil courts in other cases.

Three offences are defined under the Act, which it is unlawful either to commit, or to instruct or pressurise someone else to commit.

Direct discrimination — in which, on racial grounds, a person is treated less favourably than others would be (Section 1 & 3). Examples are:

➢ hostility, derogatory comments

➢ segregation

➢ failure to appoint someone because of their origins, colour or nationality

Indirect discrimination — in which a requirement or condition is applied equally to everyone, *but* in a particular racial group, the proportion of people who can comply with the requirement is considerably smaller than in other groups; *and* the requirement is not strictly justifiable; *and* it is to the detriment of the person who cannot comply with it (Section 1 & 3). Examples of this include:

➢ the requirement that nurses do not wear trousers with their uniforms

➢ entrance qualifications demanded which are above the statutory minimum

➢ unnecessarily high entrance/job qualifications, such as proficiency in English for a job such as laundry work

Victimisation — of a person for bringing actions under the Act (Section 2).

Two areas epitomise how uniform "colour-blind" employment practices may discriminate against black and ethnic minority people.

➤ **Advertising** — Advertising posts in traditional British news media and through the internal networks and grapevine of "white" organisations often bypasses the usual information networks used by black and ethnic minority people.

➤ **Educational qualifications** — Racial inequalities in our education system, and the consequent under-employment of black and ethnic minority people are often not recognised. Where traditional academic qualifications and experience are required for health and welfare positions many black and ethnic minority people will, therefore, be excluded, although they might otherwise be well qualified (through relevant personal experience and attributes).

EQUAL OPPORTUNITIES IN EMPLOYMENT: A CODE OF PRACTICE

In 1983, the Commission for Racial Equality published a *Code of Practice* (CRE, 1983a) for the elimination of discrimination and the promotion of equality of opportunity in employment. It gives practical guidance on the provisions of the Race Relations Act, and makes recommendations on the implementation of equal opportunities policies.

Although imposing no legal obligations, the Code's legal weight stems from its provisions being admissible as evidence in any Industrial Tribunal proceedings brought under the Race Relations Act.

Employers' responsibilities to ensure equal opportunities in employment are set out in the Code, which recommends the adoption, implementation and monitoring of an equal opportunities policy. The Code recommends action to implement an effective policy:

➤ allocation of overall responsibility to a senior manager

➤ discussion and agreement about the policy and its implementation with trade union and employee representatives

➤ ensure the policy is known to all job applicants and to individual employees

➤ regular review of employment procedures and criteria, changing them if they discriminate unlawfully

➤ base-line analysis and regular monitoring of the racial composition of the workforce

Equal Opportunities Policies are discussed further in Chapter 8, page 193. (See also Pearson (1985) and King's Fund Equal Opportunities Task Force (1988) for practical guidance.)

Popular mythology says that black professionals ... are hard to find. The experience of services and projects which have made a concentrated effort on this front ... shows this is not the case. Agencies and schemes need to review where and how they advertise their jobs and publicise their services to ensure potential black applicants are aware of openings that exist. They need to review their practices to make sure that they do not inadvertently discriminate against black candidates. In the case of black staff they need to be sure that professional qualifications required (e.g. CQSW) are indeed the most relevant qualifications for the post. Might not other qualities and expertise, e.g. being able to speak relevant languages and relate well to local communities be more important? The experience of trying to provide better services within the Asian communities supports the analysis of Lena Dominelli (1988) and others that the traditions of white "professionalism" (keeping distance from the client, only getting involved in issues directly related to the service being offered etc.) may prove inappropriate and unsuccessful with many black and ethnic minority families.

(POONIA AND WARD, 1990)

Genuine Occupational Qualifications

Under the Race Relations Act, it is unlawful to discriminate on "racial grounds" in recruitment (Section 4(1)) and in the treatment of present employees (Section 4(2)).

Discrimination is *not* unlawful in recruitment, training or promotion, however, if membership of a particular racial group as defined by the Act, is deemed to be a *Genuine Occupational Qualification* for the post (Section 5). For example:

➤ the provision of personal services promoting the welfare (such as counselling) to a particular racial group, when those services can best be provided by someone who belongs to the same group

Under the Sex Discrimination Act, being female (or male) can also be a Genuine Occupational Qualification for certain jobs.

Ideas In Practice

Social Workers in Training Scheme

Sandwell Social Services Department established its Social Workers in Training Scheme in January 1988, with the twin aims of helping solve the department's recruiting problems and at the same time redressing the imbalance of too few black workers in an area which has a 16 per cent black population. The scheme was initially set up with 20 places, half of which were to be set aside for black people. It represented the kind of action that was felt to be necessary for an effective equal opportunities policy.

Advertising was done through local papers. The focus was on attracting individuals who did not have previous experience to enter social work training. The emphasis was on individuals' personal qualities, with account taken of work they had previously done in the community.

The response was overwhelming, with half the 300 applicants from black and ethnic minority communities. The field was so good that the number of posts was increased to 18 (12 taken by people from Afro-Caribbean and Asian backgrounds).

The scheme offered two years' training — rather than the usual one — in consideration of the different routes taken by applicants reaching it. In the event not everyone needed the extra time. Five secured places on courses prior to commencing the scheme and were able to pursue professional training within the first year. The remainder all obtained places on a CQSW course subsequently.

(From Wilson, 1990)

Access Courses

Under Section 37 of the 1976 Race Relations Act, there is scope for training bodies to give access to relevant training for people from racial or ethnic minority groups who are under-represented in certain occupations or grades (see previous page and Chapter 8, Working Towards Antiracist Services). Under these circumstances, training bodies can take positive action to provide training solely for the under- represented group. Access to Nursing and Access to Social Work courses are now beginning to be developed in various educational institutions throughout the country.

Marginalisation of Black and Ethnic Minority Staff

Black and ethnic minority staff, especially those from cultural and religious backgrounds similar to service users', are vital to the provision of multiracial services. Experience shows that employing staff who can communicate with people for whom English is a second language, or who do not speak English at all, can and does result in a startling increase in service uptake by black and ethnic minority people.

A recent survey by the DHSS Inspectorate in Kirklees illustrated this point very clearly (Dearnley et al, 1986). The survey covered three areas — Batley, Fartown and Dewsbury. In Batley, where there was a team with Asian staff, an estimated 17% of the total clients referred were Asian, compared with 11% of Batley's population. In Dewsbury, with a similar proportion of the population who were Asians, but no Asian workers, only 3% of the total clients referred were Asian.

Black and ethnic minority staff will experience the same training and will be subjected to the professional norms, policies, practices and role models as their white colleagues. It is, therefore, important not to assume that they will necessarily be skilled, confident and feel supported to work from an antiracist and multicultural perspective.

Several problems emerged in our discussions with staff:

➢ the particular perspectives, experiences and skills of black and ethnic minority staff are often undervalued within services

➢ black staff become known as the "race experts" which relieves white staff of their moral and professional responsibilities in this domain

➢ black staff often feel restricted to "ethnic minority" work and prevented from using their full range of professional skills. This limits their future promotion and job opportunities

➤ some initiatives and methods which black and ethnic minority staff develop as more relevant and useful approaches are seen as unprofessional by their colleagues and managers

These criticisms have ranged from the accusation of "over-identification with the clients" to "oppressing the individual with family and community expectations" and "hindering the liberation of the individual". In some instances, black professionals were even given the choice of either being "loyal to social work agencies" or becoming "advocates for their clients".

(AHMAD, 1988)

At the *Sharing Experiences* Conference in London (Baxter, 1990a), black and ethnic minority staff working with people with learning difficulties identified several issues of concern:

➤ difficulties in helping black people to establish their own cultural identity within a white institution

➤ challenging the racism of white clients and their parents

➤ the dilemma of having to support black clients to choose between a range of inappropriate services because nothing adequate is really available

➤ equal opportunities policies have not had any real impact on racism in establishments

➤ managers may not be supportive of antiracist training, often using staff shortages as a reason for not releasing people to attend

➤ poor promotion prospects for staff who challenge the system

SPECIALIST STAFF

The 1976 Race Relations Act enables employers to seek and encourage applicants for jobs from black and ethnic minority communities. Positive action in employment practices is encouraged, the aim being to create equality of access to jobs.

Many agencies have employed black and ethnic minority staff as specialists in response to the need to make services more accessible and appropriate to the whole community. This can be a useful approach to rectifying the shortage of trained black and ethnic minority professionals. Section 11 of the 1966 Local Government Act encourages local authorities to employ extra teachers, housing officers, social workers and other staff to help "Commonwealth immigrants" whose language or culture differs from the rest of the community. Up to 75% of such specialist workers' salaries are funded directly from central government. This source of funding is

IDEAS IN PRACTICE

Recruitment of Black Staff by Nottingham Social Services

One area in which there is a considerable shortage of Asian staff is in domiciliary services. Nottingham Social Services department succeeded in attracting a significant number of Asian staff.

Approximately 10% of the population of Nottingham is black, from a wide variety of backgrounds. A recent radical approach of the Social Services Department to recruit domiciliary services staff was very successful. The areas to which close attention was paid were advertising, the use of open days and the interviewing process.

An advertisement indicating a clear commitment to recruiting black staff was translated into three Asian languages and sent to Afro-Caribbean and Asian community centres, including temples. Accompanying the advertisement was an English version and a covering letter to the leader of each Centre or community explaining the aims and objectives of the recruitment campaign. Local Asian and Afro-Caribbean radio programmes were also used.

An open day was organised in morning, afternoon and evening sessions. It provided an introduction to the work of the service and in particular the role of care assistants, job descriptions and conditions of service. The concept of multiracial service delivery was explained, covering aspects of hygiene, disability, food, shopping and language.

There were also two group sessions. One involved separate groups for black and white applicants to consider working in a multiracial community with colleagues and clients of different races. Applicants were invited to consider experiences of racism and ways of dealing with it.

Finally, applicants were able to have individual consultation and help with completing forms if necessary.

All who had come and completed a form were guaranteed an interview. Forms included details of ethnic origin for monitoring purposes.

As a result of this and further initiatives, the number of black staff in the domiciliary services rose from 12 to 60, or 84% of the Nottingham domiciliary workforce.

(FROM BEAVER ET AL, 1989)

frequently used by local authorities, but is not available to health authorities. Concern in central government that Section 11 funds have leaked into councils' general spending, rather than being used to provide specific, practical services to black and ethnic minority communities, has led to recent reforms which will require projects to be concerned with specific needs, with measurable targets and results.

Specialist black and ethnic minority staff employed on Section 11 funding often face particular difficulties:

➤ because they are appointed for their skills of language and knowledge of minority cultures, they may feel that their ethnic origin is seen as the only thing they can contribute to the service

➤ they frequently have unclear job descriptions, inadequate training, poor salary scales and no career structure, which means they often have a low morale

➤ they do not have access to decision making and are rarely given the support to raise issues which they may feel are important but which may be considered controversial

SUPPORT FOR BLACK AND ETHNIC MINORITY STAFF

The appointment of black and ethnic minority staff to work in an organisation is only a first step. They must be given the necessary support to contribute fully to the development of services and implement equal opportunities policies in their organisations.

An increasing number of local authorities have encouraged black workers' support groups. These groups help workers to:

➤ discuss their common difficulties and share their experiences of racism in a supportive environment

➤ discuss the department's policies in the context of providing a better service delivery to the black and ethnic minority communities

➤ establish a basis for change

Health authorities and voluntary organisations could learn from the experiences of local authorities in making better use of their staff and supporting them in this way.

Black Professional Support Groups

There are now a number of professional organisations set up to support black workers in their field. For more information, contact them at the addresses given (see box below).

SUPPORT GROUPS FOR BLACK PROFESSIONALS

Association of Asian Social Workers
(Contact: Theo Fariduddin)
8 Collingwood Street
London E1 5RF
Tel: 071 375 0025

Association of Black Social Workers and Allied Professions (ABSWAP)
1 Birbeck Hill
West Dulwich
London SE21 8JS

Black Health Workers and Patients Group
259a High Road
Tottenham
London N15
Tel: 081 809 0774

Anti-Racism Advisory Panel
British Association of Social Workers (BASW)
16 Kent Street
Birmingham B5 6RD
Tel: 021 622 3911

Professional Afro/Asian Women's Association
6 Adler House
Maitland Park Villas
London NW3 2EL

Race Equality Unit
National Institute of Social Work
5–7 Tavistock Place
London WC1H 9SS
Tel: 071 387 9681

Special Interest Group for Clinical Psychology (Race and Culture)
Secretary
125a Penhill Road
Bexley
Kent DA5 3EU
Tel: 0322 29322

References

Ahmad B (1988): "Community social work: Sharing the experience of ethnic groups". *Social Work Today,* 14 July, p 13.

Baxter C (1990a): *Sharing Experiences to Challenge Practices. A Report of Two Workshops around Services for Black People with Learning Difficulties.* London, CCETSW. Forthcoming.

Beaver R, Hendry B and Marston S (1989): "A more positive attitude". *Insight,* 24 January, pp 19–20.

Commission for Racial Equality (CRE) (1983a): *Code of Practice for the Elimination of Racial Discrimination and the Promotion of Equality of Opportunity in Employment.* London, CRE.

Commission for Racial Equality (CRE) (1983b): *Ethnic Minority Hospital Staff.* London, CRE.

Commission for Racial Equality (CRE) (1987): *Ethnic Origins of Nurses Applying for and in Training — A Survey.* London, CRE.

Dearnley J and Milner I W (1986): *Ethnic Minority Development (Kirklees MDC).* London, Social Services Inspectorate, Department of Health and Social Security.

Dominelli L (1988): *Anti-Racist Social Work.* Basingstoke, Macmillan.

Dominelli L (1989): "An uncaring profession? An examination of racism in social work". *New Community,* 15(3), pp 391–403.

Doyal L, Hunt G and Mellor J (1980): *Migrant Workers in the National Health Service.* London, Polytechnic of North London.

Health Service Journal (1989): "Black staff on low grades, monitoring reveals". June 1, p 656.

King's Fund Equal Opportunities Task Force (1987): *A Model Policy for Equal Opportunities in Employment in the NHS.* London, King's Fund.

Mares P, Henley A and Baxter C (1985): *Health Care in Multiracial Britain.* Cambridge, National Extension College/Health Education Council.

Pearson M (1985): *Equal Opportunities in the NHS. A Handbook.* Cambridge, National Extension College/Training in Health and Race.

Poonia K and Ward L (1990): "Fair share of the care". *Community Care,* 11 January, pp 16–18.

Torkington N P K (1983): *The Racial Politics of Health — A Liverpool Profile* Liverpool, Merseyside Area Profile Group, Department of Sociology, University of Liverpool.

Wilson M (1990): "Positive Action". *Social Work Today,* August 2, pp 22–3.

FURTHER READING

Baxter C (1988): *The Black Nurse: An Endangered Species.* Cambridge, National Extension College/Training in Health and Race.

Lunn T (1989): "Continuous agitation". *Community Care,* 13 July, pp 23–25.

MacMillan I (1989): "Black students' fate researched". *Community Care,* 22 June, p 2.

Working Towards Antiracist Services

To me, we don't go anywhere while people are "if"-ing and "but"-ing. A clearer stance on policy is needed.

Karen Salewski, Development Worker,
Harlesden Community Mental Handicap Team

Introduction

Personal and institutional racial discrimination are among the major obstacles to access to appropriate services for black and ethnic minority people with learning difficulties. Members of the caring professions would greet any suggestion that racial discrimination is intentional with offence and anger. Although there are instances of personal racism, few would deliberately withhold services or treat service users unfavourably on the basis of their colour, ethnic origin or culture. However, more subtle, indirect, manifestations of racism (Chapter 7, Black and Ethnic Minority Staff) demand a way forward to challenge its consequences.

This chapter describes how some individual service providers and managers with wider responsibilities have taken action to develop strategies to counter the impact of racism and to improve services for black and ethnic minority people with learning difficulties. It is not a recipe for radical change but demonstrates that change towards a more equitable service is possible.

- ➢ Individual Action
- ➢ Team Action
- ➢ A Corporate Equal Opportunities Strategy
- ➢ Involving Black and Ethnic Minority Communities in Service Planning
- ➢ Staff Development and Organisational Change
- ➢ The Way Forward

Individual Action

The development and maintenance of an antiracist strategy will place demands on individual service providers. Professional codes require that staff make efforts to ensure that they work effectively on behalf of all their clients, and safeguard their interests. Every worker at any level can play a part in creating a better service for the individuals with whom they are involved.

The following account demonstrates the initiative of one individual service provider.

I had always been aware of the nature of racism as it existed within institutions, but I don't feel that I fully understood the extent of its effect upon people living in the community until I met Carol.

Carol is a young black woman who was rehoused after a short stay in hospital. The area into which she was relocated was primarily white, upper middle class. Carol's flat was one in a group which housed elderly people. It has a security system which allows contact to be made with a mobile warden. The environment is sheltered.

It had been recognised that for many reasons, inclusive of the racism of people living in the surrounding area and the general solitude of the immediate vicinity, that this was not a suitable location for Carol — that being separated from people of her own cultural background and being placed in such an elderly community reinforced her feelings that she was "different" from other people. I heard these points being brought up again and again at meetings but no-one actually tackled the problem, other than to make vague commitments to relocation so I decided that I needed to try to do something myself.

There's more to antiracism than a token black worker doing 'missionary' work OK.

I spoke to Carol and she agreed that she would like to make friends and mix with other black people. After this I spoke to almost every black person I knew. Finally, a friend suggested I take her to the West Indian Social Centre. My heart sank at the suggestion. I had the same racist stereotypes in my head as many other white people and was afraid of going there at night, and was especially afraid of going into a club used primarily by black people. This realisation horrified me, but at the same time I knew my friend to be a respected member of the black community and this knowledge knocked down some of my internal barriers. I spoke to Carol and she was eager to go so we set a date.

I was very nervous of our possible reception but an ex-colleague, a man who worked with a young black man, John, said they would like to come along. As it happened, my hesitations were unnecessary. The people could not have been more welcoming. They paid us the compliment of accepting us all without question. Although we received the occasional glance, no-one stared and when Carol and John went to the bar, they accepted it without any query and even though John couldn't speak they directed their enquiries to him, not us.

John loved it — from the moment we arrived and now over a year later still goes in. John has many of the characteristics of autism, thus he doesn't make much eye contact or get involved in too much touch and my proudest recollection is one night when a steel band was on, we had all crowded around the stage and I felt him take hold of my hand. I was very pleased.

Carol was more reticent, self critical and lacking in both self esteem and confidence. It was a while before she would go on the dance floor and when she did, her movements were awkward and rigid. But she gained her confidence in this environment and tried to learn to dance, and most important was asked to.

As the positive aspects became more apparent, I became more conscious of the social gap that existed for black people who had no choice other than to live in all white environments.

It is a small, simple task to take people to a social club once a month. It doesn't cost much in terms of time and money. Yet it brought so much to Carol, John and Ray and probably more to me. I would recommend it to anyone.

We have all been going for over a year now and still feel it is very worthwhile.

RESIDENTIAL MANAGER

Setting Up a Group for Black Clients at an ATC

Questioning policies and practices can place individuals in a painful dilemma. They may fear that well intended questions will result in inaction or even reprisals. There is a feeling of powerlessness as a lone individual in big and bureaucratic systems. Staff need support to take individual action to improve their professional performance in this area. One member of staff at an ATC opted to work closely with a group of clients from an inner city catchment area, among which there was a higher than average ratio of black and ethnic minority clients.

I soon realised that during a large part of the person's life — attending the day centre — specific needs of black clients were being noticeably overlooked, even ignored.

I often heard nicknames and jokes with racist overtones being aimed at those clients who were usually very upset by these comments. One man who has a speech problem was made fun of because of this and was called a tribal sounding name by staff and clients alike. He was noticeably uncomfortable in this situation and deeply disliked being made fun of. His communication difficulties at the centre may have been enhanced because he lived in a home environment where a pronounced West Indian Patois was used.

Another client was very withdrawn and depressed and would go for days without eating; often locking herself in the toilets, crying for hours on end. As our relationship evolved, she built up enough trust in me to open up verbally.

She felt very isolated and that people were laughing at her. She often referred to her skin colour and made comments like, "People don't like me because I'm black". She used the word "nigger" to describe herself.

Other things overlooked at the centre were the dietary requirements of ethnic minority clients, music and just having positive images of black people around the centre. Also, the fact that racist attitudes and comments were allowed to continue unchallenged. Another problem was that there were no black staff employed at the centre, with the exception of the occasional supply worker, student or YTS, all of whom were temporary.

I felt there was a strong case for setting up a self advocacy group for black clients run by a black volunteer, for them to explore any issues that arose for them in a safe environment. They may have wanted to explore nicknames and labels, request the kitchen to put on a more varied menu, the council to employ more black staff.

The manageress and another staff member were very supportive at the time. However, there was strong resistance from members of staff who didn't like the sound of my group as it would segregate the black clients and make them stand out from the others.

A black woman student on a social work access course ran the group, but there were problems in getting those clients who wanted to attend the group together at the same time. One left the centre, another was on work training.

I then decided to change tack slightly and set up a multicultural/development education group which would not be quite so radical, but one of its aims would be to challenge and hopefully eliminate some of the racist attitudes and stereotypes held by clients at the centre.

The group ran for 20 weeks and was highly successful. We explored food, dance, language and music from other cultures. We looked at inequalities and human rights. We related this, using a game, to the apartheid system. We used art and collage to illustrate "one world" and movement of people in the world. Finally, we made a carnival costume from scrap materials.

There should be more education to raise awareness of staff on the issues around black people with learning difficulties and an attempt not to employ people with racist attitudes. A two day antiracist training course does not solve the problem.

There should be a recognition of the needs of black clients and an attempt to meet these needs at day centres — not to treat everyone as if they are white.

ATC WORKER

Team Action

The strength in numbers of a team approach is likely to result in a bigger impact on local services than individual action can secure, as the following example of an initiative of one Community Mental Handicap Team shows (Open University, 1990).

Harlesden Community Mental Handicap Team

Our work with both black and white families has improved since we questioned the norms in mental handicap work.

Harlesden Community Mental Handicap Team (HCMHT) covers an area of the London Borough of Brent. It is a multiracial area with a significant African, Caribbean, Asian and Irish population. The population on the whole suffers from a high level of deprivation and disadvantage.

➢ **Initial concern about racism and mental handicap** — When HCMHT was established in 1984 there was an awareness that services for people with a mental handicap were not being shared equally by all potential users of services. Staff felt that courses about how to work with "ethnic minorities" did not address the issues around them. On one course a parent spoke of her experience as a black parent not receiving the same service as her white neighbour. She spoke graphically of the lack of understanding and support from health and social services.

➢ **Establishing parents' opinions** — In November 1984 a questionnaire about local services was sent out to families of people with learning difficulties. The main objective was to find out users' opinions of services, what improvements were wanted and what action staff could take.

There were clear differences in the answers given by black and white respondents. For example, the majority of white parents did not want more contact with other parents or more information/workshops on handicap, whereas the majority of black parents did.

The Mental Handicap Register showed that despite equal numbers of black and white people with a mental handicap, the majority of black people were cared for by their families whilst the majority of white people were in some form of residential/hospital care.

➢ **Antiracist training** — Staff worked with the department's Race Training Development Officer to look at training needs. The team undertook a valuable antiracist training course. It facilitated reappraisal of attitudes and highlighted the whole area of double discrimination.

IDEAS IN PRACTICE

Nottingham Race Strategy and Mental Handicap Implementation Group

A multidisciplinary group, consisting mainly of health and social workers, was established in 1983 to improve services for black and ethnic minority service users and their families by working with and supporting managers and staff.

In 1987 the group carried out a sample survey of black families of people with learning difficulties (Nottingham SSD, 1987). Since then its main focus has been on implementing the recommendations formulated after the survey.

The group has recently been involved in ensuring that appropriate meals are provided at social services day care and residential centres in

Nottingham. With the involvement of an Asian social worker, an Asian Carers Group has also been established. The group is currently looking at establishing appropriate antiracist training for staff within health and social services.

Contact: Mike Lee
Research Officer
Social Services Department
County Hall
West Ridgeford
Nottingham NG2 7QP

Tel: 0602 823823 ext 3953

➤ **Changing practice** — It became clear to the team that their practice needed to change. They established a black parents' support group to ensure that black parents had a forum in which to meet each other and offer mutual support. (Mencap locally fulfilled this role for white parents.)

The team also questioned the application of normalisation and the cultural bias of assessments. The concept of "over-protectiveness" could be seen as appropriate protection in the face of double discrimination.

➤ **Training package** — A training package was needed to ensure that all staff had the opportunity and direction to change their own practice. Three day training was offered to health and social services personnel. It included sessions looking at their own attitudes, their origins, their own racism and what they needed to change in themselves and in their current work. Personal commitments needed to ensure change were identified, and the need for monitoring of the change recognised. Future training, therefore, included managers.

All staff, at whatever level, can influence practice. Receptionists can ensure that the office is welcoming to all users with appropriate posters and literature on display. Staff with direct contact with families can ensure that they do not undermine families through their practice but enhance and look positively at the contribution that families make.

For a fuller account of Harlesden Community Mental Handicap Team's work, see the Open University course K668 *Mental Handicap: Changing Perspectives,* Audio Cassette 2, Side 2, "Making a Case for Change II", and accompanying *Media Notes* (Open University, 1990).

Lewisham Contact a Family

In 1986 Lewisham Women's Committee gave funding to Contact a Family to employ a black worker (as a Genuine Occupational Qualification under Section 5 (2) of the Race Relations Act) to look into the under-representation of black families in the membership of Lewisham Contact a Family (a self-help group for families with children with special needs). There were two main areas of concern:

➢ the low numbers of black families amongst Lewisham Contact a Family members, and the low rate of referral from agencies in the borough

➢ the low level of involvement of black families in the organisation's activities

The project had two strategies:

➢ **External work** — strategies aimed to encourage local agencies to refer black families

➢ **Internal work** — strategies for Contact a Family itself to change its own image and practice and work positively with black families

The research and development worker appointed to the project, Frances Fletcher, interviewed local black and ethnic minority mothers. Their comments were very similar: "I felt like the odd one out", "I felt excluded", "I felt isolated". Several of them said that they felt Contact a Family was "a white organisation" and "worked for white families only".

Like many other statutory and voluntary organisations, Contact a Family in Lewisham at that time made little provision to accommodate people whose first language was not English. Information was not translated into other languages and there was no recognition of different cultures and religions in the material available. For most black families, this white image deterred them from joining the group.

A questionnaire was circulated to establish the range of ethnic minorities and different languages spoken locally. Then the group took a number of steps to change the white image of the organisation.

➤ The local newsletter began to acknowledge different cultural events and festivals and translate items where possible.

➤ Contact a Family events and meetings tried to foster a multicultural image through providing different foods from different cultures.

➤ Voluntary interpreters were provided for people who needed them.

➤ The local office used posters and leaflets in different languages.

It was hoped that these changes would create a more welcoming atmosphere for black and ethnic minority families and would educate white English families about other cultures and make local agencies more aware of the importance of referring black families to Contact a Family.

Separate Afro-Caribbean and Asian parents' support groups were established. Previously, black parents had:

➤ gone along to a Contact a Family meeting and felt excluded and uncomfortable

➤ been put off from going along by Contact a Family's "white" image, anticipating that they would feel "different" from other parents attending

➤ never been referred to Contact a Family

The black support groups allowed black mothers to be involved in Contact a Family on their own terms. Mothers commented on the importance of having meetings in their own homes, feeling comfortable in each other's company and being able to relate to one another. None of this had been the case for black parents previously attending Contact a Family groups.

The Asian support group gave Asian mothers a chance to be with people who understood their culture and language. It helped to break down their sense of isolation — something which is common to all mothers of children with disabilities but reinforced for Asian mothers by their experiences of living in a society which does not recognise their culture.

Of course, Lewisham Contact a Family's initiative encountered some difficulties. Some white families were concerned at the idea of a black worker being employed to work with black families. They felt this to be a segregatory strategy which diverted resources specifically to black families. They were unaware that black parents had not previously received a fair share of resources. It was assumed that black parents did not use local services because they did not need them. At the same time, some older Afro-Caribbean parents were also worried that separate support groups might be segregatory. Contact a Family's workers, however, felt that separate groups could give black parents the kind of support that they needed.

In fact, the strategies adopted by Lewisham Contact a Family were successful. There was an increase in the number of black parents referring themselves to the organisation, and its membership gradually began to reflect more closely the multiracial composition of the local community.

(Source: Contact a Family, 1989a; Open University, 1990, Audio Cassette 3, Side 1, "Make a Case for Change III", and accompanying *Media Notes*.)

A Corporate Equal Opportunities Strategy

Any real change in the nature of services requires a comprehensive strategy for action. Managers wishing to respond to this challenge have the 1976 Race Relations Act to support them (see Chapter 7, Black and Ethnic Minority Staff). The Act recommends the implementation of equal opportunities policies.

Equal opportunities policies are underpinned by the principle that all individuals and groups of people have a right to accessible and appropriate services and that some users are currently disadvantaged because of their gender, race or disability. Policies aim to:

➢ eliminate discrimination

➢ promote equal access

➢ develop services which respond to the needs of disadvantaged groups

An antiracist policy would ideally tackle simultaneously racism in employment and service delivery.

In Chapter 7 we suggested that if the staff providing services do not reflect the local population, services will be unable to respond effectively to the needs of the whole community. Some health, education, local authorities and voluntary organisations have begun to develop and implement equal opportunities policies. Some of the important aspects of equal opportunities in employment have already been explored in Chapter 7. Parallel initiatives to improve equality of access to services have not gathered the same momentum. This section, therefore, focuses on a strategy for provision of services.

Principal elements of an equal opportunities strategy should include:

➤ a clear commitment to reject and challenge racism, overt and covert

➤ a review, in consultation with local minority communities, of established policies, procedures and practices to identify how and where services are failing to meet the needs of black and ethnic minority service users

➤ drafting and implementation of strategies for change (including service objectives, specific action plans, and time scales)

➤ allocation of responsibility for the policy's implementation to a senior manager

➤ monitoring and assessment of the impact of initiatives and changes implemented

People with learning difficulties from black and ethnic minority communities are doubly disadvantaged and any strategy addressing their needs must include specific service objectives encompassing both race and disability.

Our questionnaire survey of health authorities, social services departments, education authorities and community health councils established that, as with equal opportunities policies in employment, social service departments have taken the lead in formulating policies for service provision.

IDEAS IN PRACTICE

Enfield Social Services Department Joint Action Plan:
Learning Difficulty and Physical Disability Services

The Joint Action Plan was the response to the Social Services Department's recognition that their poor communication and relationship with ethnic minority communities prevented them from:

➢ informing families about services

➢ responding to their perceptions of social services

➢ reviewing services with them

➢ having a workforce representative of the local community

Aim

To provide appropriate and accessible services to disabled members of the black and ethnic minority community within the context of normalisation and related principles

Objectives

➢ to inform black disabled people and their families about the Social Services Department's and related agencies' services

➢ to present to black disabled people a positive image of Social Services and their underlying principles

➢ to consult, review and reform services with service users, including black disabled people

➢ to establish a workforce that is representative of the community it serves

Strategy

To achieve the aim and objectives, a series of geographically based time limited development schemes will be established, that will set up a network of contacts with the ethnic minority communities and the disabled people within them. The scheme will:

➢ identify effective conventional communication methods and use them as a means of making contact with the ethnic minority community

These methods might include the ethnic minority press, newsletters, individual mailshots, public meetings, consumer surveys etc.

➢ consult with existing Section 11 workers, established groups and organisations for black disabled people, religious organisations and CRC

➢ identify key staff as named contacts within establishments, who will act as a focus of communication with black disabled people

➢ The communication process will be effective only if it is interactive. It will, therefore, seek the views of ethnic minority communities and their disabled members, but mechanisms are required that will convert their responses into action, producing a service that both follows normalisation principles and is ethnically sensitive. At an operational level, the Service Managers and R and D Manager for physically disabled services will form a management group, but senior managers will need to consider their responsibilities and roles.

(BOX CONTINUED OVERLEAF)

Ideas In Practice (continued)

Strategy (continued)

➤ It is recommended that a post of linkworker development officer be established. The post holder's task would be to set up communication and consultation systems as described above, but staff in the establishments would be required to operate them. The post holder would, therefore, be a facilitator and not be seen as the specialist in communicating with ethnic minority communities.

➤ The first development scheme will be centred on Dewsbury Day Centre and Ravensthorpe SEC. The management group will meet as soon as is practical to set timescales and inaugurate the first scheme.

Contact: Enfield Social Services Department
8th Floor
Civic Centre
Silver Street
Enfield

Tel: 081 366 6565

Putting Policies into Practice

Of course, equal opportunities policies on paper will not change the experiences of either black and ethnic minority service users or workers. For this to happen, agencies will need to take active steps to translate their policies into practice (See Pearson (1985) for a practical guide to the implementation of equal opportunities policies.) Sadly, experience suggests that this is rare (Brown, 1989). Authorities keen to improve their performance in this area will need to ensure that fine words are followed through with positive action for change.

IDEAS IN PRACTICE

Equal Opportunities and Services for People with Mental Handicap

EXTRACT FROM "BETTER SERVICES FOR PEOPLE IN LEEDS WITH A MENTAL HANDICAP"

Needs of Minority Ethnic Groups

The Authorities aim to develop services to take account of the needs of people from all ethnic groups. Attention will be given to ensuring that people from minority ethnic groups are aware of the full range of services available. The views of people from minority ethnic communities should be sought when services are being planned so that differing needs arising from religious or cultural factors are understood and appropriate provision made. The development of befriending and advocacy schemes should assist in helping to identify different needs. Voluntary organisations, especially those within minority ethnic communities, will also be able to contribute towards the development of services in a way that is sensitive to the needs of minority ethnic groups. There will be special factors to take into consideration in residential, day and community settings, and in ensuring that families receive appropriate support through services such as the family placement scheme, advocacy and befriending schemes.

1. Introduction

There are two aspects of the subject of equal opportunities in relation to services for people with mental handicap. The first is that people with mental handicap are themselves a minority group and the philosophy underpinning the whole of the strategic plan is that they should be valued as full citizens and given the same opportunities in life as other people. This includes giving them appropriate support in using these opportunities so that the only limiting factor is their disability.

The second aspect is that all people with mental handicap, regardless of their racial, religious or social background, age or gender should have the opportunity to benefit from appropriate services. It is on this aspect that this paper will concentrate.

2. The Issues

A preliminary view suggests that the following issues may need to be addressed:

(a) flexibility in service provision to respond to particular needs arising from cultural or religious backgrounds

(b) dissemination of information about available services

(c) development of staff understanding of:

　(i) different naming systems

　(ii) different religious and cultural observances

　(iii) different perceptions of mental handicap and appropriate responses to it

(d) provision for language difficulties

(e) flexibility in catering arrangements to meet different dietary requirements

(f) monitoring and evaluation arrangements

Revisions to this list may, of course, be necessary in the light of information gained at a later date.

(BOX CONTINUED OVERLEAF)

Needs of Minority Ethnic Groups (continued)

3. The Tasks

3.1 The first and fundamental task must be to develop an understanding of the attitudes to mental handicap of the various ethnic minority groups represented in the city and the service needs arising from them. Information about a variety of associations representing ethnic minority groups has been supplied by the Equal Opportunities Unit, and it is proposed that contact should be made with as many of these as possible. Another source of information is voluntary organisations, particularly those who are making specific attempts to reach ethnic minority groups, e.g. Sharing Care, Leeds Advocacy.

3.2 Having established this information base it will then be possible:

(a) to provide a checklist for service planners and providers to enable them to build the necessary flexibility into services

(b) to develop staff training in sensitivity to religious or cultural differences and their effects

(c) to make the necessary provision for language differences

(d) to make any necessary adjustments to catering arrangements

3.3 Another aspect will be to ensure that the appropriate information about available services is disseminated to ethnic minority groups. The contacts built up in the course of the information gathering exercise described in paragraph 3.1 above will be helpful here.

3.4 Finally, monitoring and evaluation arrangements will need to be instituted to measure the effectiveness of this work. The computerised register currently being compiled will include information about the uptake of service by minority groups, but will need to be in the context of the proportions of ethnic minority groups in the population and the prevalence of mental handicap among them.

Contact: Malcolm May
Principal Adviser
(Mental Handicap)
Leeds City Council
Sweet Street
Leeds LS11 0DQ

Tel: 0532 463435

Involving Black and Ethnic Minority Communities in Service Planning

If services for black and ethnic minority people with learning difficulties are to improve, black and ethnic minority people must be involved in service planning and provision, and black and ethnic minority organisations must be consulted for their views. Individual representatives should be co-opted on to relevant authority subcommittees and working parties.

Since many voluntary organisations do not reflect the needs of black and ethnic minority communities, complete reliance on traditional (predominantly white) voluntary organisations will not be sufficient to ensure adequate representation of black and ethnic minority people on local authority committees. The challenge to ensure adequate consultation and representation is, therefore, one that exists for both voluntary organisations as well as statutory.

The most popular forms of ethnic minority consultation are co-opting or electing representatives on to existing committees and the formation of special race relations committees/subcommittees, consultative panels or working groups.

If authorities' equal opportunities strategies are to be effective in involving the whole community, certain pitfalls must be avoided.

➤ The aims and objectives of meetings are often not made explicit to black and ethnic minority communities so that they may not be aware of what is expected of them, and what their own contribution might be. They are consequently ill-prepared for a positive input into the process.

➤ The criteria for nominating, selecting and electing co-optees should be clearly thought through by both the local authority and the organisations concerned, to avoid confusion which could lead to mutual distrust.

➤ Representatives should have previous knowledge about the local communities, preferably speaking the relevant language(s).

➤ Meetings should take place in a familiar environment. For example, a local community hall or religious institution, like a gurdwara, which may have space for such meetings, or a local health clinic familiar to people in that area.

➤ It has to be made easy for people to attend meetings. This may entail holding a meeting during the weekend, when people are less likely to be working, or after working hours. Transport must be provided where necessary.

➤ People's wishes concerning the organisation of the meeting have to be respected. For example, men and women may prefer to sit separately.

- ➢ Priority has to be given to facilitating good communication. Interpreters must be provided where necessary.

- ➢ How much power does the chairperson have and what is his/her attitude to ethnic minorities, people with learning difficulties and to consultation and consumer involvement?

- ➢ Who sets the agenda? Are those co-opted asked or consulted on items?

- ➢ Do those co-opted have speaking and voting rights? (Even with these rights are they still in a minority?) Are they informed of meetings in time? Are they given the necessary back-up, support and background information?

- ➢ How will decisions be followed through and action taken on issues raised and discussed in committees/meetings?

Local authorities may have some form of consultation arrangement through specially employed personnel (for example, Section 11 workers, development workers, project or linkworkers). These workers are usually relatively junior and unless special effort is made to involve them, they tend not to have any real access to policy and decision makers.

Authorities may wish to consult umbrella organisations for advice on issues of community race relations. This may be preferred because it provides an easy, identifiable channel of communication, and is less time consuming. Community relations councils are the longest standing bodies to play this role. They are particularly useful in their knowledge of existing local community groups and resources (although it is possible that their directories are sometimes limited to the larger and well known organisations and are, therefore, better used in conjunction with other sources of this type of information).

Differing Needs of Different Communities

All too often black and ethnic minority people are viewed as homogeneous communities. Agencies adopt the approach of consulting so called "community leaders" or "community representatives" about the needs of their communities. Class, gender, political and religious persuasions exist among all people in society. Black and ethnic minority people are no exception. Black and ethnic minority people are individuals in their own right. Consultation processes have to avoid this type of pitfall. It is important to ensure that individual committee members are truly accountable to any organisations which they may represent.

There will be instances where formal structures may not necessarily be the most effective route to consultation. It might be appropriate to develop informal approaches as well. Working parties, public meetings, talking to community groups as well as interested, active and concerned individuals and other such informal arrangements can all co-exist and complement formal committees.

Meeting people on their own ground may prove to be the most effective way to come face to face with issues of concern to the community. Such exercises are useful starting points in the process of sensitising local authorities and may also be a good vehicle for two way exchanges of information. In isolation, however, they are not effective ways of fostering community participation in decision making.

There is no single easy way that consultation may be best achieved. Local and health authorities and other agencies may find the process slow and time consuming. What is certain is that if better service delivery is to result, there needs to be the determination to change and make appropriate provisions, even where this means the revision of priorities, timescales or the reallocation of funds.

Pressure from outside will always be necessary to keep organisations mindful of the communities they serve. Continuing dialogue with these communities is important.

STAFF DEVELOPMENT AND ORGANISATIONAL CHANGE

Education and training have a key role to play in bringing about change. They are an integral part of implementing an equal opportunities programme.

Existing training programmes fail to prepare professionals to provide services from a multiracial perspective. Most programmes are still carried out on the assumption that students are going to work only with clients from a homogeneous white, Anglo-Saxon, Christian oriented culture. Social workers and care providers (including nurses, doctors and other health workers) are taught about practical care, food and diet, interpersonal skills and family relationships from standpoints which assume shared cultural values and behaviour patterns of one kind. This has to change.

Training on Culture — A Dangerous Practice

Much training to meet the needs of multiracial service users has previously been centred around cultural information. The rationale has been that teaching about other cultures would create understanding and tolerance. This assumed that all cultures were equally valued in British society and ignored the central issue of racism and the impact which this has on policy, practices and people's experiences. It is now becoming accepted that this kind of approach is outdated, although it still exists in pockets across the country. The danger is that, without questioning their attitudes, service providers may acquire information with which they may stereotype people further. For these reasons teaching based specifically on the "cultural information" model should be rejected.

Training and Organisational Development

Staff development is about good professional practice. A training initiative such as the one by Harlesden Community Mental Handicap Team referred to earlier in this chapter is one example of how an organisation can take on the issue of antiracism.

It is vital that this kind of work does not take place in short one-off workshops. These are of little use and can be counterproductive. The subject needs to be integral to all training, not treated as an unusual and special topic. The success of antiracist training will depend largely on the level of commitment of senior managers in confronting racism. This will enable consolidation of training in the workplace.

To address the double discrimination of people with learning difficulties from black and ethnic minority communities, antiracist training will need to be linked to Disability Awareness Programmes. Disability Awareness Programmes (or Training) are based on a political analysis of disability. The main emphasis is on creating an awareness that discrimination against people with disabilities, including learning difficulties, is often perpetuated by institutions and individuals who are commonly seen as working on their behalf.

It is important that people who are involved in staff education and development are capable and competent. Black and ethnic minority people themselves should be involved in teaching and facilitating such programmes. They will be able to identify the gaps and ways in which services are inappropriate in a way white people are not able to do. Involving people with learning difficulties wherever possible in training events for staff is important and will have a powerful impact.

The major part of training budgets of most health and welfare organisations is traditionally spent on further advancing the careers of the most advantaged sections of the workforce. Little effort is directed towards lower paid, less skilled and undervalued staff at the bottom of the hierarchy. A disproportionately high number of black people are concentrated in this section of services. They do not, therefore, have the same access to training as their white counterparts.

➢ Between 1983 and 1986 a total of 2000 people went through Normalisation and PASS workshops run by the training section of the Community and Mental Handicap Educational and Research Association (CMHERA). Participants were drawn from Newcastle, Derbyshire, Manchester, Lancashire, Bristol and elsewhere. The workshops were advertised within local authorities and health authorities and local training co-ordinators were relied on to recruit and organise participants.

➢ Out of a total of 2000 participants, only 5 were from black and ethnic minority communities and these were all either doctors or psychiatrists. One of the CMHERA training co-ordinators involved was concerned about the absence of black participants and contacted the London Association of Community Relations Councils about this. It was suggested that the advertising of workshops should in future explicitly encourage invitations from people from black and ethnic minority communities to apply. Local co-ordinators should also be asked why there were no black applicants and what their plans were for rectifying the situation.

Those responsible for staff development and training generally would do well to follow this advice when organising their development programmes — and to monitor the extent to which black and ethnic minority staff are getting access to the training provided.

IDEAS IN PRACTICE

Caring in Homes Initiatives — Training for Care Assistants

The National Institute of Social Work is developing a series of training packages for residential homes. The three year project will provide home owners and managers with a staff training pack.

The training will be aimed at care staff who are often unqualified and employed in low paid manual grades. Part-time staff who are mainly women from black and ethnic minority communities and who have little sense of career structure will be targeted.

The pack will also be addressing issues about the provision of services for a multiracial clientele. The Institute's Race Equality Unit will be involved in input to this aspect of the pack. For further information, contact:

Penny Youll
University of West London
Uxbridge
Middlesex UB8 3PH

Tel: 0895 56461

IDEAS IN PRACTICE

CCETSW North England Curriculum Development Project in Antiracist Social Work

The CCETSW North England Curriculum Development Project in Antiracist Social Work ran two events in March and April 1989. The aims were to:

➤ provide information on the debates, discussions and strategies concerning antiracism in contemporary Britain

➤ ensure wider recognition of the need for social work education to counter its racist and ethnocentric ideas and practices

➤ identify and address black students' and social workers' concerns in social work curricula

➤ exchange antiracist perspectives on key issues pertaining to social work education and practice

➤ identify and organise issue-based groups to work on specific elements of curriculum development in social work, with a view to producing materials in Phase 3 (from April 1989)

The ultimate aim of the regional subgroup is to provide education and training materials in antiracism in working with children and families, elders, mental health, learning difficulties, probation practice teaching.

A core text of key articles in race, racism and antiracism will be published in 1990 which provides the context for the above six areas. It is anticipated that materials for the six areas will be published by early 1991.

Contact: Naina Patel
CCETSW
26 Park Row
Leeds LS1 5QB
Tel: 0532 431516

Ideas In Practice

The London Based Training Consortium (LBTC)

The London Based Training Consortium (LBTC) is currently working on a project funded by the Central Council for the Education and Training of Social Workers. The aim is to research training needs and produce training materials in the area of antiracist practices in the provision of services to people with learning difficulties.

Four activities have been carried out so far:

➢ a workshop (SEARCH conference) in which black service users and their carers shared their experiences of using services

(The Sharing Experiences Conference has been described earlier, on page 146.)

➢ a workshop (SEARCH conference) for service providers which provided a forum for discussion and clarification of practice issues for services operating in a multiracial society

➢ a Training the Trainers Workshop for experienced teachers of staff who were working with people with learning difficulties and/or had experience of training with an antiracist perspective

➢ detailed indepth interviews with four or five black potential users (people who did not use services) and their carers

Interviewers were bilingual and from similar backgrounds to their respondents.

The aim of these activities was to get to grips with practice issues from both the clients' and the service providers' perspective and then to produce staff development materials for antiracist practices in services for people with learning difficulties.

It is anticipated that materials may take the form of a combination of self-learning, group learning, and trainers' handbooks. Case studies

from the interviews will also be used to demonstrate and highlight the individual needs of families, to avoid the amassing of cultural information.

The report of the LBTC's two SEARCH conferences, *Sharing Experiences to Challenge Practice* (Baxter, 1990a), identifies the following components of an antiracist training package:

1. Racism

An understanding of the origins, nature and mechanism of racism is crucial to people's engagement in, and commitment to antiracist strategies. Specifically, programmes in this area should give participants an understanding of:

➢ the historical, social and political context of racism

➢ Race Relations legislation and codes of practice for Equal Opportunities, and local and health authorities' legal obligations

➢ the effect of racism on established services

— the overarching prevalence of unspoken white, largely protestant, male and middle class assumptions and values which underpin our services and professional training

— the "colour blind" approach which results from those limited assumptions

— stereotypes and other negative images of black people as service users and providers

➢ the impact on black and ethnic minority service users

— inappropriate and irrelevant care

— misdiagnosis and inappropriate treatment

— lack of racial and community identity

— low individual self-esteem

(BOX CONTINUED OVERLEAF)

IDEAS IN PRACTICE (CONTINUED)

The London Based Training Consortium (LBTC) (continued)

2. Antiracist Practice

Unless training also includes ways of positively and effectively challenging direct and institutional racism, participants may be disempowered and overwhelmed by the impact of racism. Training and staff development packages should, therefore, include:

➢ challenging racism in service users

➢ challenging racism in other staff

➢ developing support mechanisms and structures for black service users

3. Implications of Philosophies of Care and Policy for a Multiracial Society

➢ normalisation

➢ care in the community

➢ the "five accomplishments" (O'Brien, 1986)

➢ individual programme plans

➢ "an ordinary life"

4. Personal Physical Care

Training in practical skills in relation to individual needs in the following:

➢ hair care

➢ care of skin

➢ food and dietary preferences

➢ leisure time activities

5. Working with Families

Staff should have an understanding of:

➢ how family structures *may* differ in black and ethnic minority communities

➢ how to establish, sensitively, an individual's family circumstances, avoiding stereotyping

➢ family dynamics and the principles of family therapy

6. Resources in the Community

To enable and encourage community presence and participation, staff should be aware of:

➢ how to identify local minority community organisations and initiatives

➢ how to approach, and be involved with, local organisations

7. A Multiracial Team

➢ the principles and dynamics of teamwork

➢ the need for role and task definition

➢ an awareness of how racism might jeopardise team working relationships

➢ sharing skills and power

8. Black Workers' Support Group

White and black staff should understand the need for, and positive role of, black workers' support groups:

➢ how racism is internalised in professional education and by black people who go through the training process

➢ how to keep involved in antiracist activity, and support Equal Opportunities initiatives

➢ the need for support when individuals challenge the system, often in highly marginalised and isolated positions

9. Working Effectively with Interpreters and Advocates

➢ appreciating their principal loyalty to clients

➢ the need for respect of their role

➢ confidentiality

Contact: Peter Richies
LBTC (Training for Care)
9 Tavistock Place
London WC1H 9SN
Tel: 071 388 2041

THE WAY FORWARD

The enormity of the challenge to implement antiracist strategies to improve services for black and ethnic minority people with learning difficulties may be daunting to many people. It is vital, however, that service providers do not become paralysed by the scale of the task. Many of the projects and initiatives which we have cited in this handbook demonstrate the scope for achieving real change at a local level. Whilst piecemeal initiatives should be avoided if possible, individuals, teams, units and entire organisations have a part to play in implementing systematic change in their own area of practice.

In the absence of initiatives in the statutory services, a growing number of black and ethnic minority people and organisations have begun to establish their own services and training initiatives, as many of the examples of "Ideas in Practice" which we have cited in this handbook demonstrate. These initiatives, though scattered, are to be warmly welcomed. We hope that readers will take heart from the examples we have given, and find ways of implementing similar changes in their own work.

The Need for Action

Concerted action is needed at all levels of the community, voluntary and statutory services.

➤ Central government should ensure that changes in funding arrangements do not threaten the already precarious interests of black and ethnic minority people with learning difficulties. Where possible, statutory and voluntary agencies funded by central government should be *required* to demonstrate their commitment to the provision of services which meet the needs of black and ethnic minority people.

➤ Statutory agencies should review their services to ensure that the needs of all groups are met, so that community care can become a reality for the whole community.

➤ Voluntary agencies should assess whose needs they meet and articulate. Are they adequately representing black and ethnic minority people's concerns?

➤ Black and ethnic minority organisations should ensure that they represent the needs and concerns of people with learning difficulties, and of their families. Where consultation with service providers on race equality issues is underway, the interests of people with learning difficulties should be integral to the agenda for change.

A Checklist for Action

In working towards racial equality in services for people with learning difficulties, several issues will need to be addressed, and action taken. Some of these will have particular relevance to residential services, for example, whilst others may be more pertinent to other kinds of provision, such as education. We list them together here, because a *systematic approach* to your organisation's services will avoid the pitfalls of adopting an ineffective piecemeal approach.

➢ **The local black and ethnic minority population** — Service providers and voluntary agencies should ensure that they know their whole local community.

— A demographic profile is essential to establish whom services should be reaching in black and ethnic minority communities.

— Contact should be made with local black and ethnic minority organisations. The local Community Relations Council should have a list, and may have a health and welfare officer and sub-committee with whom contact should be made.

— There may be black and ethnic minority staff working in services for people with learning difficulties who are active in their own communities, and would be in a key position to articulate their community's needs.

— Unmet need should be estimated, by looking at the demographic and social profile of local communities, consulting with black and ethnic minority organisations and professionals, and monitoring the existing use of services.

➢ **Current services**

— Do they reflect the needs and concerns of the local black and ethnic minority communities?

— Do established policies, procedures and practices permit a flexible response to individual needs?

— Are services as currently provided socially and physically accessible to black and minority communities?

— To what extent are current services taken up by local minorities? A monitoring exercise may need to be implemented.

— Does your organisation have a multiracial staff, reflecting the local population and able to communicate and relate to them?

— Do you have a multiracial group of service workers and carers, to ensure that all people in day services, residential placements or respite care can be appropriately supported?

➤ **Racism** — We have cited some instances in which crude or more insidious, subtle racism has resulted in appallingly unprofessional standards of care, and very real distress and damage for black and ethnic minority people with learning difficulties.

— Has it been made quite clear to staff (and volunteers) that expression of racial prejudice is totally unacceptable, and may be a disciplinary offence?

— Are staff aware of how their own, silent, prejudices can alienate black and ethnic minority people, and deter them from using services?

— Are staff aware of how black and ethnic minority people can be alienated by established policies, procedures and practices which largely reflect white, professional norms?

➤ **Communication** — We have seen how many of the problems and stresses faced by people with learning difficulties and their families can be exacerbated by language differences and communication problems. It is easy to forget just how alienating professional jargon and ways of working can be.

— Are bilingual staff, advocates and/or trained interpreters employed to ensure that staff working in the service are able to communicate with all clients?

— Do you have counsellors who are able to communicate with, and relate sensitively to, local black and ethnic minority families? Are counselling services widely publicised in the minority communities?

— Is all your information about available services and assessment procedures translated into the relevant languages, with use of audio and visual media, and the black and ethnic minority press or radio/ TV programmes as appropriate?

— Is there a need for home–liaison staff from the local minority communities, who can visit families in their homes and make that service more accessible to them?

— Have monolingual, English-speaking staff been given training to ensure that they appreciate that people in Britain speak different languages, and how to work effectively with trained interpreters?

➤ **Activities and curricula** — It is important that the curriculum and activities of schools, adult training centres and other organisations working with people with learning difficulties reflect the daily lives of black and ethnic minority people.

— Do educational curricula reflect the everyday customs and practices of black and ethnic minority people?

— Are single sex activities provided, as appropriate?

— Are assessment tests and procedures relevant to the everyday life and language of the person with learning difficulties, or are they underpinned by white, professional norms and assumptions?

— Do the activities offered positively reflect and cater for black and ethnic minority leisure pursuits?

— Have links been made with local black and ethnic minority organisations and employers who may be able to offer employment or activities for people with learning difficulties?

➤ **Everyday care** — Individual needs cannot be met unless services are able to cater for a range of personal preferences and practices.

— Do staff have a sensitivity to the variety of preferences and practice in everyday life, the dangers of indulging in cultural stereotypes and the need to establish what individuals prefer and require?

— Do catering arrangements take black and ethnic minority diets and preferences into account?

— Are staff competent at looking after different skin and hair types?

— Can different religious requirements be catered for?

— Do service policies reflect the diversity of family circumstances in multiracial Britain?

➤ **Implementing change** — Is easier if you can "take people with you", and if objectives are clear to all concerned.

— Has your organisation adopted a formal antiracist or racial equality policy, making its commitment to challenge racism clear?

— Are local black and ethnic minority organisations aware of your policy and commitment? Have they been active participants in the process of change?

— Are all staff (and volunteers) aware of the organisation's commitment to promote racial equality in its service provision and employment? A formal statement would assist them.

— Is a senior member of staff clearly responsible for implementation of the policy? Do people find her/him accessible?

— Is there an action plan, with clear targets and delegated responsibilities, for implementation of the antiracist strategy?

References

Baxter C (1990a): *Sharing Experiences to Challenge Practice. A Report of Two Workshops Around Services for Black People with Learning Difficulties.* London, CCETSW. Forthcoming.

Brown B (1989): "Race: Needed — Policy and practice perspective". In Philpot T (ed): *The Residential Opportunity? The Wagner Report and After.* Wallington, Reed Business Publishing/Community Care.

Contact a Family (1989a): *Reaching Black Families? A Study of Contact a Family in Lewisham and the Relevance of Services for Black Families who have Children with Disabilities and Special Needs.* London, Contact a Family

Nottingham SSD (1987): *Sample Study of Black Families with a Mentally Handicapped Member.* Nottingham Social Services Department. Unpublished.

O'Brien J (1986): "A guide to personal futures planning". In Bellamy G T and Wilcox B (eds): *A Comprehensive Guide to the Activities Catalogue: An Alternative Curriculum for Youth and Adults with Severe Disabilities.* Baltimore, Paul H Brookes.

Open University (1990): *Mental Handicap: Changing Perspectives,* Course K668. Milton Keynes, Open University, Department of Health and Social Welfare.

Pearson M (1985): *Equal Opportunities in the NHS. A Handbook.* Cambridge, National Extension College/Training in Health and Race.

Further Reading

Larbie J, Mares P and Baxter C (1987): *Trainer's Handbook for Multiracial Health Care.* Cambridge, National Extension College/Training in Health and Race.

Mares P, Henley A and Baxter C (1985): *Health Care in Multiracial Britain.* Cambridge, Health Education Council/National Extension College.

Information Exchange

The King's Fund Centre is establishing a health and race information exchange focusing on health and social services issues for people from black and ethnic minority groups.

The exchange will provide a forum for people to share ideas and experiences and learn about developments in other parts of the country. It is hoped that the exchange will highlight some of the gaps in provision nationally and encourage both statutory authorities and voluntary community groups to develop new initiatives.

For information on the learning difficulties component of the information exchange, contact:

> Yvonne Christie or Linda Moore
> Community Living Development Team
> King's Fund Centre
> 126 Albert Street
> London NW1 7NF
>
> Tel: 071 267 6111